# HANDS-ON START TO
# WOLFRAM|ALPHA
## NOTEBOOK EDITION™

# HANDS-ON START TO
# WOLFRAM|ALPHA
## NOTEBOOK EDITION™

*Cliff Hastings*   *Kelvin Mischo*

## Wolfram Media

Champaign

## Wolfram Media, Inc.

*Hands-on Start to Wolfram\Alpha Notebook Edition*
Copyright © 2020, Wolfram Media, Inc.
www.wolfram-media.com
Champaign, IL 61820-7237, USA
ISBN 978-1-57955-039-4 (paperback)
ISBN 978-1-57955-040-0 (Kindle)

Library of Congress Cataloging-in-Publication Data

Names: Hastings, Cliff, author. | Mischo, Kelvin, author.
Title: Hands-on start to WolframAlpha Notebook edition / Cliff Hastings,
  Kelvin Mischo.
Description: First edition. | Champaign : Wolfram Media, Inc., [2020] |
  Includes index.
Identifiers: LCCN 2020041083 | ISBN 9781579550394 (paperback) | ISBN
  9781579550400 (epub)
Subjects: LCSH: Mathematics--Study and teaching--Computer network
  resources. | Expert systems (Computer science) | Educational technology.
  | AMS: Mathematics education -- Educational material and media,
  educational technology.
Classification: LCC QA11.5 .H378 2020 | DDC 510.78/5633--dc23
LC record available at https://lccn.loc.gov/2020041083

Final typesetting and page production were completed using Wolfram Notebooks.

Printed in Canada. ∞ Acid-free paper. First edition. First printing.

# Table of Contents

# INTRODUCTION
# How to Use This Book

## Create Examples while Reading

This book is meant to be an active companion during the process of learning how to use Wolfram|Alpha Notebook Edition and Wolfram|Alpha (WolframAlpha.com). The main body of the text will provide a collection of useful calculations to demonstrate how the software works, and the examples should be retyped by the reader as a starting point for individual projects and exploration of the software. Each chapter contains discussion, tips and a description of how Wolfram|Alpha Notebook Edition works, along with actual examples that serve as starting points. Each chapter ends with additional exercises, which can be assigned to students or used for additional practice for the reader.

No matter what format this book is viewed in, it is recommended that readers have Wolfram|Alpha Notebook Edition accessible either as a local installation or available within a browser to type examples and work through the exercises. It is recommended that as readers work through the book, they save a new file for each chapter in Wolfram Notebook format (.nb), either locally or in the Wolfram Cloud, for future reference.

 Any text in this type of styled box is meant to be a tip by the authors. The advice is meant to pass along experience gained from teaching many people how to use Wolfram|Alpha Notebook Edition.

## Goals for the Chapters in This Book

Chapters 1 and 2 in this book outline sample projects created in Wolfram|Alpha Notebook Edition to provide a guide for the reader on what is possible after reaching a basic level of understanding of the software. These chapters contain only minimal explanation of how to create similar projects or supplemental materials for a course, and are instead designed as a jumping-off point for readers to inspire their own ideas on how to use the software.

Chapters 3, 4 and 5 outline Wolfram|Alpha Pro and focus on how to use the website for various calculations and projects. The chapters focus on step-by-step solutions for a wide variety of problems, as well as how to upload external data files for analysis and how to download results.

Chapters 6, 7, 8, 9 and 10 outline Wolfram|Alpha Notebook Edition and focus on how to create notebooks with a mix of calculations and nicely formatted text for projects or supplemental materials for a course. These chapters focus on entering basic calculations, word processing, creating presentations in the from of slide shows and sharing projects or course materials after they have been created in the software.

Chapters 11, 12, 13, 14 and 15 outline how Wolfram|Alpha Notebook Edition can support specific topics in mathematics, including prealgebra, algebra, trigonometry, precalculus, calculus and statistics. These chapters outline more specific calculations related to the respective chapter topics to provide a more detailed starting point to using the software in those areas.

## Wolfram|Alpha Notebook Edition on the Desktop and in the Browser

Wolfram|Alpha Notebook Edition includes an option for installing software to a local machine and running notebooks on that local machine, as well as an option to use the software within a browser with a login and password. In either case, the experience in the software is largely the same, and the examples in this book can be created in either environment.

That being said, some of the capabilities related to creating nicely typeset formulas exist only in a local installation. A reader might work through the examples in this book on a laptop with a local installation of the software, or a reader might work through the examples on a tablet or Chromebook within a web browser. The book will outline how to work with files and will show how to use different types of devices interchangeably.

## Getting Access to the Technology in This Book

If a reader does not currently have access to Wolfram|Alpha Notebook Edition, a trial license can be downloaded at the following website: wolfr.am/wanetrial.

Wolfram|Alpha Pro is available on a monthly basis at a low cost to gain access to that technology while reading this book as well. Additional discounting is available for students: www.wolframalpha.com/pro/pricing.

## Getting Answers to the Exercises

You can request an answer key by visiting the webpage at www.handsonstart.com/wane-key and entering the unique code associated with your book. This eight-character code can be found on the inside of the back cover of the book. The page is entirely blank except for the code printed toward the bottom of the page.

Requesting the answer key will also allow you to receive special offers and free extras to help you get started with Wolfram|Alpha Notebook Edition.

## Other Wolfram Technology

Besides Wolfram|Alpha Notebook Edition, some other Wolfram technologies and services are used or mentioned in the book, many of which are available at no additional cost. Most references to technologies other than Wolfram|Alpha Notebook Edition are things that are incorporated into Wolfram|Alpha Notebook Edition. No products other than Wolfram|Alpha Notebook Edition and Wolfram|Alpha Pro are needed in order to successfully work through the examples in this book. The majority of the chapters, with the exception of chapters 3, 4 and 5, require only Wolfram|Alpha Notebook Edition and do not require Wolfram|Alpha Pro.

# CHAPTER 1
# Sample Projects in Wolfram|Alpha Notebook Edition

## The Scope of Wolfram|Alpha Notebook Edition

Released in 2009, WolframAlpha.com is a unique engine for computing answers and providing knowledge with a workflow of inputting calculations in plain, everyday English. Rather than requiring a specific sequence of commands or a specific sequence of choices in a set of menus, WolframAlpha.com accepts many different styles or phrasings to describe a calculation. Since various people have different styles of working and computational backgrounds, this approach makes the website useful to a large audience for a wide variety of calculations.

Wolfram|Alpha Notebook Edition includes the same convenient format for entering calculations in everyday English. While WolframAlpha.com, or Wolfram|Alpha as a shorter name, is designed for single calculations through a website interface or a mobile app, Wolfram|Alpha Notebook Edition is local to your machine and designed with the cloud in mind. It handles multiple calculations and aids in building up ideas and showing a collection of calculations all in one environment. The notebooks in Wolfram|Alpha Notebook Edition can include titles, text, graphics, imported images, live calculations, animations or slide show presentations. This means Wolfram|Alpha Notebook Edition has the simplicity of Wolfram|Alpha to enter a series of calculations, while also including a rich document format, which is the same format included in Mathematica.

This chapter will demonstrate the process of starting with two real-world problems and exploring solutions in Wolfram|Alpha Notebook Edition through a series of calculations, visualizations and textual explanation. Subsequent chapters will provide a more granular explanation of how Wolfram|Alpha Notebook Edition works for specific types of calculations or in specific areas; this chapter is meant to illustrate what is possible after achieving a basic understanding of working with Wolfram|Alpha Notebook Edition.

 This formatted text is meant as a comment for the reader, and these comments will be interjected throughout all chapters in the book. For example, this entire book was written in Wolfram|Alpha Notebook Edition; each chapter was created as a different Wolfram Notebook file.

## Project 1: Projecting the Hours of a Summer Job

### Details of the Project

Michelle Abacus has two goals for her summer break. Her first goal is to increase her savings account from $225 to $3,000 from her summer job so she can pay for her apartment over the first semester at college. Her second goal is to take as much vacation time as possible just prior to the start of the fall term.

Michelle can work a maximum of six hours per day at minimum wage as a lifeguard, and can only work complete weeks (starting on a Monday and ending on a Friday). Her summer break begins on May 21, 2020, and ends on August 1, 2020, and she lives in Amherst, Massachusetts, USA.

Assuming Michelle has no expenses over the summer while living at home and she saves money as quickly as possible, when can she stop working as a lifeguard and start her vacation prior to the fall semester?

### Is the Savings Goal Possible?

One of the first pieces of information that is needed to calculate Michelle's earnings is the hourly wage when working as a lifeguard. In this case, Wolfram|Alpha has built-in data to provide her hourly wage, which is the minimum wage in Massachusetts.

$12.75 per hour

Notice the software returns units along with the hourly wage. Mousing over the result of the calculation creates a pop-up with more details about the unit. Wolfram|Alpha Notebook Edition has a large collection of units spanning many fields and areas.

Before calculating too many details, it would first be useful to calculate if Michelle's goal is possible, even with no vacation. Wolfram|Alpha Notebook Edition understands dates and calendar information very well, and can aid in quickly determining the longest possible duration Michelle can work over the summer. For example, her break starts on May 21, 2020, which this calculation shows is a Thursday.

The process of creating calculations will be outlined in later chapters in much more detail, but typing any of these phrases into the software should automatically create the orange bounded input field to enter a calculation. Pressing the Enter key will perform the calculation and display the result.

Since Michelle can begin working only on Mondays, the software can provide the date of the following Monday.

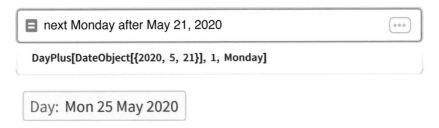

Michelle's latest possible end date for her summer job can be calculated in a similar manner. Wolfram|Alpha Notebook Edition can return the nearest Friday prior to the start of her fall semester.

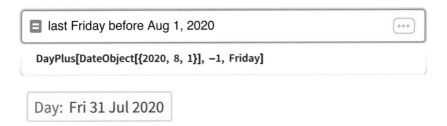

With a specific start date of May 25 and an end date of July 31, Wolfram|Alpha Notebook Edition can calculate the quantity of weekdays in that span of dates. To count complete days rather than partial days, the calculation uses the Sunday prior to May 25 and the Saturday after July 31.

50 weekdays

 Counting days using Sunday and Saturday (instead of Monday and Friday) might seem counterintuitive, but calculations can be used to count hours, or seconds, or any span of time. Since partial days are rounded down (they are not complete days), using the date of the corresponding weekend days provides a count of complete days.

Based on a total of 50 weekdays and working 6 hours per day, Michelle can work a total of 300 hours over the summer if she takes no vacation, and assuming the pool is open each of those days.

300 h

To determine whether Michelle's goal is possible, a single input can be used to calculate the total quantity of hours Michelle can work, along with her hourly wage and her existing savings.

$4 050.00

> Although units have been returned in other calculations, the calculation above actually reduces the units and returns a result in dollars. This is handy to confirm the methodology for the calculation is accurate.

This verifies that Michelle can definitely reach her savings goal of $3,000 over the summer since she would earn $1,050 more than her goal if she takes no vacation time. The next step is to calculate the balance between working days and vacation days to achieve her second goal of taking the maximum number of vacation days at the end of the summer.

### Graphical Estimate When Michelle Will Earn $3,000

To calculate the quantity of days Michelle can allocate to vacation at the end of the summer break, the first step is to determine exactly when she will be able to save $3,000 or more. Wolfram|Alpha Notebook Edition can be used to create a large variety of graphics to help visualize this overall relationship, while the exact result will be calculated later in the chapter. The following calculation generates the equation for a line based on the two known points calculated above. The $x$ coordinate represents elapsed days and the $y$ coordinate represents her savings level. Recall Michelle started with $225, and the calculation above provided $4,050 as her savings level if she works all 50 possible days over the summer.

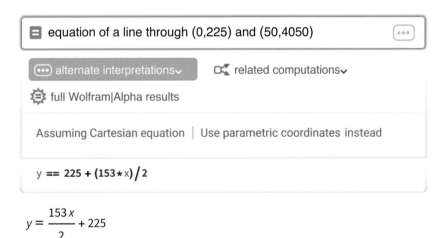

$$y = \frac{153\,x}{2} + 225$$

That result can be graphed to inspect the $y$ axis, corresponding to Michelle's level of savings.

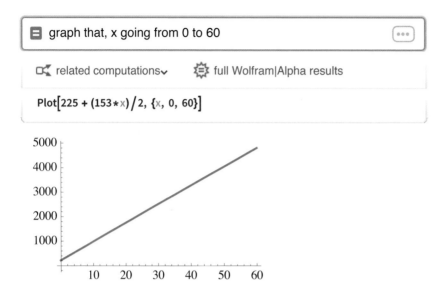

The term "that" will be discussed throughout this book as a useful shortcut. Also, the phrase "x going from 0 to 60" is not required to generate a graph, but is useful in this case to show only positive values since $x$ represents time.

Through visual inspection, the value $3,000 on the $y$ axis lines up with roughly 36 days on the $x$ axis. This visual inspection can be verified by repeating a previous calculation with a value of 36 working days instead of 50.

$2979.00

The result is very close to $3,000, and provides a good estimate for the final answer.

## Exact Calculation When Michelle Will Earn $3,000

While the above graphical inspection, along with a trial and error approach, provides a solid intuition for the desired result, Wolfram|Alpha Notebook Edition can perform a wide variety of algebraic calculations to provide a more exact result. Approaching a problem using multiple methods is also a useful way to confirm results. The following example repeats a calculation from the previous section to return the equation for a graph corresponding to the two known points.

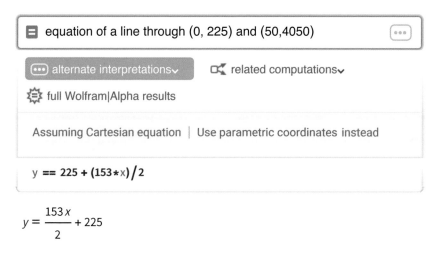

$$y = \frac{153\,x}{2} + 225$$

Wolfram|Alpha Notebook Edition can also substitute specific values for variables in an equation. For example, to further confirm this equation represents the desired results, a value of 50 days can be substituted for the variable $x$. The result is $4,050, which matches the calculations above and verifies the equation is the desired relationship.

| | |
|---|---|
| ▤ y = (153/2) x + 225 where x = 50 | (•••) |

⚙ full Wolfram|Alpha results

> y == (153/2)*x + 225 /. {x -> 50}

$$y = 4050$$

Solving equations for a particular variable is straightforward as well. By using a value of $3,000 for *y*, Wolfram|Alpha Notebook Edition can solve for the value of *x*. The result is in exact form, and provides the exact quantity of days when Michelle will achieve her savings goal.

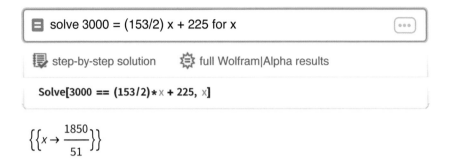

$$\left\{\left\{x \to \frac{1850}{51}\right\}\right\}$$

The arrow notation above is used to show solutions in the form of a rule. This means the variable *x* is still a symbol and can be used for other completely unrelated calculations. Storing specific values with variable names is possible, and will be outlined in a later chapter.

Instead of a fraction, the term "previous result" can be used to round the fraction to five digits for a numeric approximation.

$$\{\{x \to 36.275\}\}$$

Michelle will achieve her savings goal in 36.275 days. If she can somehow convince her supervisor to allow her to work partial days (and partial weeks), she could very precisely achieve her goal.

Alternatively, if a calculation involves a decimal approximation, the result is returned as a decimal approximation. The previous "solve" calculation can use a decimal to consolidate the previous two calculations into one calculation.

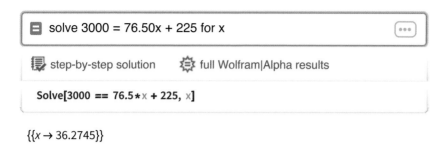

$\{\{x \rightarrow 36.2745\}\}$

However, one of the original assumptions was that Michelle could not work partial days, nor partial weeks. To account for this, the following input takes the first day of work, May 25, 2020, and adds 37 weekdays to see exactly which day could be her first day of vacation (assuming she could work partial weeks).

By starting with Michelle's new initial vacation day of Wednesday, July 15, 2020, Wolfram|Alpha Notebook Edition can calculate the quantity of weekdays between her end date at work and the day she moves to college (August 1, 2020).

Similar to a previous calculation, Wolfram|Alpha Notebook Edition can count days, or hours, or seconds, and rounds partial days down, so the calculation above uses "July 14" and "Aug 1" to count full days.

This means Michelle can spend 13 weekdays on vacation at the end of the summer. Or, including weekends, Michelle can spend 18 days on vacation at the end of the summer and will achieve her savings goal.

> 📋 days between July 14, 2020 and Aug 1, 2020    ⋯

18 days

## Project 2: Hanging Paintings and Centering the Layout

Michelle ended up with some extra money from her summer job so she decided to purchase four paintings for her new apartment. She wants to hang her paintings in a unique pattern where they are centered on a particular wall. Two of her new paintings are two feet by two feet, while the other two paintings are two feet high by three feet wide. The total width of her wall space is nine feet. The total height of her wall space is 13.5 feet.

Michelle laid out the paintings in the following pattern and determined she wants each gap labeled $a$ to be the same distance measurement, and she wants each gap labeled $b$ to be the same distance measurement.

Similar to the unknown height values, Michelle would like the width values labeled $c$ to be same, and $d$ to be proportionally smaller than $c$. She expects the final layout to be similar to the following approximate layout.

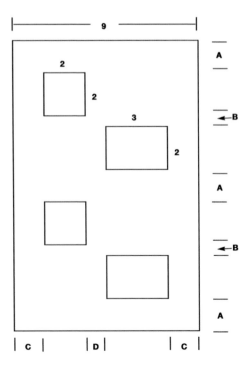

## Solve for Height Values *a* and *b*

Wolfram|Alpha Notebook Edition supports a wide variety of algebraic calculations. Entering the known and unknown height values is a good starting point to simplify the algebraic expression.

> ▤  simplify a + 2 + b + 2 + a + 2 + b + 2 + a = 13.5                    (•••)

> ⚙ full Wolfram|Alpha results
>
> **Simplify[a + 2 + b + 2 + a + 2 + b + 2 + a == 13.5]**

$3a + 2b + 8 = 13.5$

 Notice for any calculation, an additional line is created with the corresponding Wolfram Language. Although it is not a requirement, it is sometimes useful to scan through the Wolfram Language version of the calculation to confirm the calculation is the intended one. In this case, the Wolfram Language uses two equal signs in an equation. Seeing these syntax conventions is primarily useful to transition to Mathematica or another software that uses the Wolfram Language, but it is not a requirement to understand any syntax to use Wolfram|Alpha Notebook Edition.

In fact, any calculation will automatically simplify algebraic expressions, even when the input does not direct Wolfram|Alpha Notebook Edition to do so.

> ▤  a + 2 + b + 2 + a + 2 + b + 2 + a = 13.5                    (•••)

> ⚓ related computations⌄        ⚙ full Wolfram|Alpha results
>
> a + 2 + b + 2 + a + 2 + b + 2 + a == 13.5

$3a + 2b + 8 = 13.5$

The result is an equation with two unknowns, and Wolfram|Alpha Notebook Edition can work with this expression to solve for one or the other variable to reformat the equation as needed.

---

▣ solve 3a + 2b + 8 = 13.5 for b ⚬⚬⚬

✦ full Wolfram|Alpha results

Solve[3∗a + 2∗b + 8 == 13.5, b, MaxExtraConditions –> Automatic]

---

$\{\{b \to 2.75 - 1.5\,a\}\}$

 The arrow above is also a Wolfram Language convention and simply means that $b$ is 2.75–1.5$a$ for this particular calculation. Since Wolfram|Alpha Notebook Edition can perform a variety of symbolic calculations, the arrow simply denotes that the variable $b$ is still a symbol for any other calculation in the session.

## Adding More Assumptions to Arrive at Exact Solutions

While the above solution solves the variable $b$ in terms of $a$, in practice, Michelle would like to arrive at numerical results for the variables $a$ and $b$ to act as precise measurements for her paintings. One idea to accomplish this would be to choose a value for either variable to simplify the set of equations.

For example, in the following input, a value of 1.5 feet is substituted directly for the variable $a$, which then leads to an output of 0.5 feet for the variable $b$.

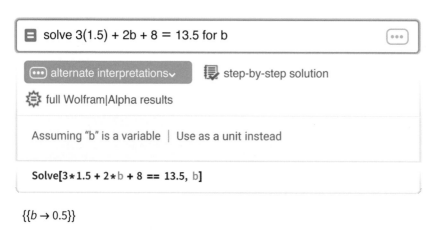

---

▣ solve 3(1.5) + 2b + 8 = 13.5 for b ⚬⚬⚬

⚬⚬⚬ alternate interpretations⌄   📋 step-by-step solution

✦ full Wolfram|Alpha results

Assuming "b" is a variable  |  Use as a unit instead

Solve[3∗1.5 + 2∗b + 8 == 13.5, b]

---

$\{\{b \to 0.5\}\}$

Multiplication can be done with an asterisk (*), a space or with the notation above using parentheses. For equations, Wolfram|Alpha Notebook Edition will even correctly interpret multiplication without any of these things. For example "2b" above is interpreted as 2 times $b$. An input of "3x5" will also be interpreted as multiplication of 3 times 5. Using "x" is usually reserved for algebraic calculations, so this is generally not good practice and one we try to avoid in this book. Otherwise, the results from "3x5" versus "(3x)5" might be counterintuitive, with the former being interpreted as multiplication while the latter is interpreted as a symbol $x$.

A second idea to arrive at specific numerical values would be to define a second equation for the relationship between the two variables. Instead of substituting a specific value for the variable $a$, the following input defines a second equation representing that the value of the variable $a$ should be twice as long as the variable $b$. Wolfram|Alpha Notebook Edition can solve two equations with two unknowns by listing them with parentheses and specifying that the desired output should solve for both $a$ and $b$.

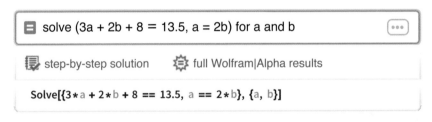

$\{\{a \rightarrow 1.375, b \rightarrow 0.6875\}\}$

The result is 1.375 feet for $a$ and 0.6875 feet for $b$. When considering the format of the output for measurement on a wall for the placement of the respective paintings, converting the output from feet to inches might be a more practical unit of measurement. Both values can be converted in the same calculation by listing them with parentheses. The result is also a list.

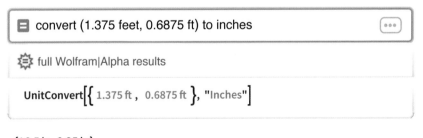

$\{16.5 \text{ in}, 8.25 \text{ in}\}$

### Solve for Width Values *c* and *d*

A similar process can be used to set up equations for the width values and obtain specific values for the variables *c* and *d* in the figure above. Entering each measurement in the figure provides a simplified equation representing the known and unknown width values.

> ☰ c + 2 + d + 3 + c = 9     ⋯

> ◁ related computations⌄     ✷ full Wolfram|Alpha results
>
> c + 2 + d + 3 + c == 9

$2c + d + 5 = 9$

Since this equation also has two unknowns, a second equation must be defined to obtain specific values. The following input solves two equations with two unknowns. The second equation specifies that the value of the variable *c* should be four times larger than the value of the variable *d*.

> ☰ solve (2c + d + 5 = 9, c = 4d) for c and d     ⋯

> ▤ step-by-step solution     ✷ full Wolfram|Alpha results
>
> Solve[{2*c + d + 5 == 9, c == 4*d}, {c, d}]

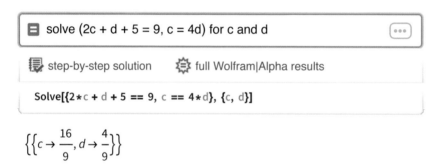

$$\left\{\left\{c \to \frac{16}{9}, d \to \frac{4}{9}\right\}\right\}$$

The following calculation creates a decimal approximation with three digits.

> ☰ previous result to 3 digits     ⋯

> ✷ full Wolfram|Alpha results
>
> N[{{c -> 16/9, d -> 4/9}}, 3]

$$\{\{c \to 1.78, d \to 0.444\}\}$$

The approach above will work again to convert the results from the previous calculation from feet to inches. Use of parentheses creates a list of values, so each value is converted to inches, and the result is also a list of values.

{21.36 in, 5.328 in}

 While previous calculations have included units or converted between units, the input above purposely uses both "ft" and "feet" to represent that particular unit of measurement. Wolfram|Alpha Notebook Edition has a vast knowledge of units and makes the correct assumption regardless of abbreviation in most cases.

Now that Michelle has calculated specific values for the variables $a$, $b$, $c$ and $d$, she can measure and hang her paintings with the desired relationships and centering.

# CHAPTER 2
# Supplemental Materials in Wolfram|Alpha Notebook Edition

## Introduction

In addition to entering calculations using everyday English, Wolfram|Alpha Notebook Edition contains a rich document environment called Wolfram Notebooks. While a common first step involves using Wolfram|Alpha Notebook Edition for calculations to support a course or real-world project, instructors find the document environment just as important to create supplemental materials for a course. This environment can be used to author materials across many fields or course topics, and this chapter will act as a guide for new supplemental materials, including a sample lecture, sample notes for students to review individually, sample exercises for students and a sample of a printed quiz or test.

While a few tips will be included within this chapter, subsequent chapters will outline how to create supplemental materials and the scope of available functionality in more detail.

## Sample Course Lesson

### Real-World Use of Variables

While it is common to use variable names like $x$ or $y$ in equations, any letter or symbol can be used as a variable, and variables often represent a specific real-world concept. Consider the concept of free-fall motion represented by this equation, where $d$ represents distance and $t$ represents time.

$$d = \frac{1}{2}(-9.8)\,t^2 + 50$$

## *Exploration*

Consider a scenario where Chris is standing at the edge of the roof of a building. The building is 50 feet tall. If Chris drops a shoe and three seconds elapse, how far above the ground will the shoe be at that point in time?

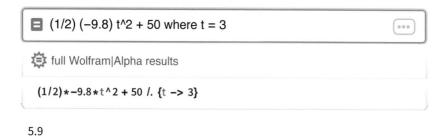

5.9

Based on this same equation, the following input shows a graphical representation of this free-fall motion for a duration of three seconds.

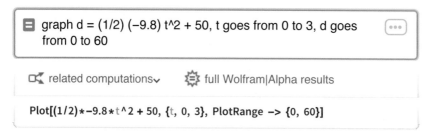

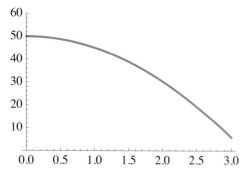

 The Exploration section could act as an example for a lecture in class, with the calculations above being evaluated live while discussing the concepts with students. The text also acts as a complete explanation of the concept so students can individually review the notebook for a quiz or test in the future.

## Practice

1. Consider the scenario above where Chris drops the shoe off the roof of a building. What is the distance above the ground after 3.1 seconds have elapsed?

 (1/2) (−9.8) t^2 + 50 where t = 3.1          ⋯

(1/2)*−9.8*t^2 + 50 /. {t −> 3.1}

2.911

---

This Practice section is designed to be a sample exercise for students or learners. A suggested approach is to save two different versions of this content: one version acting as an answer key for the author, and the second having blank spaces for the inputs that answer the exercise questions. Those blank spaces act as prompts for the recipient of the notebook to work through the exercises.

2. Create a graph for the equation above representing free-fall motion, with *t* varying from 0 to 4. Experiment with different values for *d*, where *d* goes from 0 to 50 or −75 to 50.

---

 If *d* represents distance, does it make any sense to think about a graph that goes from −75 to 50 for that axis (a negative distance)? The question below prompts the learner to think about whether that makes physical sense or not.

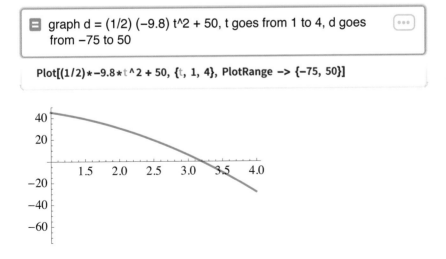 graph d = (1/2) (−9.8) t^2 + 50, t goes from 1 to 4, d goes from −75 to 50          ⋯

Plot[(1/2)*−9.8*t^2 + 50, {t, 1, 4}, PlotRange −> {−75, 50}]

3. What are the differences between the graph in question 2 compared to the graph in the Exploration section? In your own words, explain what this tells you about the real-world scenario.

Answer: when $t = 4$, the graph shows a negative distance, meaning the shoe hits the ground somewhere around 3.2 seconds. The following calculation calculates a more exact answer compared to a visual inspection of the graph.

solve (1/2) (−9.8) t^2 + 50 = 0 and t > 0

Reduce[{(1/2)*−9.8*t^2 + 50 == 0, t > 0}, t]

$t = 3.19438$

The text cell with an orange bounded box was created with the **Writing Assistant** palette. The drop-down menu for **Frame** is located in the **Writing and Formatting** section, with options for frame styles and frame coloring. If this document is meant for a student or learner as an exercise, the text cell could be blank, acting as a prompt for the learner to write text as the answer to the exercise question.

## Additional Exploration

In the previous examples, the height of the building was 50 feet. Use the following model to explore free-fall motion where the height of the building varies from 10 to 100 feet.

graph d = (1/2) (−9.8) t^2 + h, t goes from 0 to 3, d goes from 0 to 100, varying h from 10 to 100

Manipulate[Plot[(1/2)*−9.8*t^2 + h, {t, 0, 3}, PlotRange −> {0, 100}],
{{h, 55}, 10, 100, Appearance −> "Labeled"}]

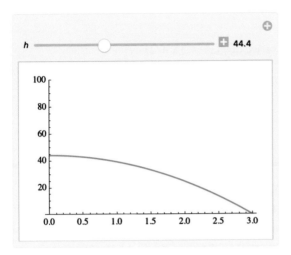

Consider the height of 44.5 feet and what the graph tells you about that real-world scenario.

---

 This Additional Exploration section could be a bonus exercise for a learner working through the exercises, or it could be a wrap-up to a lecture that bridges the current lesson into the next lesson concept.

## Sample Printed Quiz or Test

The following content is written with textual cells, which will be outlined in more detail in a later chapter. The focus of this section is to create styling that mirrors a textbook and allows an instructor to create a quiz or test that includes their favorite problems, or alternate problems if multiple versions of a quiz are necessary. These cells are more focused on styling and how the quiz looks when printed and used in a proctored test setting, and are not focused on calculations or solving the problems.

A few tips on formatting are included in this chapter, and each of these ideas will be outlined in more detail in later chapters. They are included in this chapter to act as a reference when revisiting this chapter and using it as a guide to create new quizzes or tests.

### Calculus Quiz 4

**Topics:** derivatives, tangent lines, concavity, points of inflection

Name: _____

Section: _____

Date: _____

## Questions

**1.** Which of the following is the derivative of $f(x) = 3x + 2$?

    a) $f'(x) = 2$                           b) $f'(x) = 3$

    c) $f'(x) = 5$                           d) None of the above

Since the Enter key is used for evaluation of input cells, holding the Shift key and pressing the Enter key creates a new line in a text cell. At times, this operation can change the justification of the first line of text. Clicking the **Format** menu, choosing **Text Justification**, then choosing **None** will toggle the first line of text back to the original justification.

**2.** Which of the following is the derivative of $f(x) = \pi x^7 - 2x^5 - 5x^{-2}$?

    a) $f'(x) = 7\pi x^6 - 10x^4 + 10x^{-3}$       b) $f'(x) = 7\pi x^6 - 10x + 10x^{-3}$

    c) $f'(x) = 7\pi x^6 + 10x - 10x^{-3}$       d) $f'(x) = 7\pi x^6 - 10x^4 + 10x^3$

The available symbols for plain text are a bit more extensive than the symbols available for calculations. The **Special Characters** palette within the **Palettes** menu contains many special characters and symbols available for plain text content.

**3.** Which of the following is the derivative of $f(x) = (x^2 + 17)(x^3 - 3x + 1)$?

    a) $f'(x) = 2x^4 - 63x^2 - 49x$         b) $f'(x) = -x^4 - 3x^3 - 57x^2 - 49x$

    c) $f'(x) = 5x^4 - 42x^2 + 2x + 17$      d) $f'(x) = 5x^4 + 42x^2 + 2x - 51$

Notice the formulas have a slightly different formatting compared to the other plain text sentences. This formatting can be created using the **Writing Assistant** palette located in the **Palettes** drop-down menu. First highlight the formula, then choose **Inline Math Cell** under the **Math Cells** drop-down menu to apply this different styling. To toggle back to plain text formatting, press the down-arrow key.

**4.** Which of the following is the derivative of $f(x) = \dfrac{1}{3x^2+1}$ ?

a) $f'(x) = -\dfrac{6x}{(3x^2+1)^2}$

b) $f'(x) = \dfrac{-6}{x^2+1}$

c) $f'(x) = \dfrac{6x}{(3x^2+1)}$

d) $f'(x) = \dfrac{6x}{(3x+1)^2}$

---

The 2D typesetting for fractions is also accessed in the **Writing Assistant** palette under the **Palettes** drop-down menu under the **Typesetting** section. Fractions can sometimes reduce the size of the text relative to other text, and clicking the **Formatting** menu, choosing **Size**, then choosing **Larger** is a convenient way to increase the size of the formula that contains a fraction.

**5.** Which of the following is the graph of the derivative of $f(x) = \dfrac{1}{3x^2+1}$ ?

a)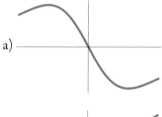

b)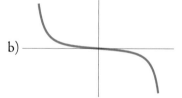

c)

d)

---

Results in the form of graphics can be resized by highlighting them, then dragging a corner to create the desired sizing. The four graphics in this multiple-choice question were created with separate calculations, then the results were highlighted, copied and pasted into the textual content, then resized to fit the page.

## Answer Key

It is common for an instructor to save two versions of a notebook file. One version could contain only the five quiz questions above, and would be printed and used in a proctored quiz. The second version of the notebook file could include the five quiz questions, which can be refined later or used as a template for other quizzes, as well as an answer key. The calculation to create the graphics for the fifth question is also included below for reuse if the quiz needs to be refined or edited in the future.

1. b
2. a
3. d
4. a
5. a

▤ graph the derivative of 1/(3x^2 + 1) with no ticks          ⋯

⟂ related computations⌄          ⚙ full Wolfram|Alpha results

Plot[Evaluate[D[1/(3*x^2 + 1), x]], {x, −0.58, 0.58}, Ticks −> None]

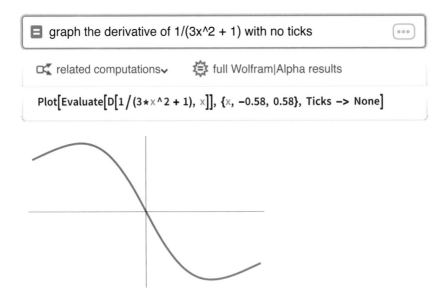

# Conclusion

Wolfram Notebook files can be saved as local files that retain all textual information, inputs for calculations, results for calculations and generated graphics. To distribute supplemental materials to students, simply send the file to students so they can work through the examples in their own copies of Wolfram|Alpha Notebook Edition. A subsequent chapter will discuss options to share materials to students as a local file, a static PDF or in the form of a URL to post materials to a class website or any place where students access course materials in a web-based format.

# CHAPTER 3
# A Basic Introduction to Wolfram|Alpha and Wolfram|Alpha Pro

## Introduction

The majority of this book outlines the capabilities of Wolfram|Alpha Notebook Edition specifically. This chapter, as well as a few subsequent chapters, will outline the capabilities of Wolfram|Alpha, which is most commonly accessed at WolframAlpha.com. Wolfram|Alpha was originally released in 2009 and has the same style of accepting everyday English for calculations as Wolfram|Alpha Notebook Edition. In fact, both use very similar underlying technology for calculations, making it easy for users of Wolfram|Alpha to learn Wolfram|Alpha Notebook Edition.

## Wolfram|Alpha Technology

Wolfram|Alpha is freely available for single calculations, and a Pro subscription is available to extend attributes of what the free version provides. Both the free and Pro versions can be accessed with a web browser or a mobile app and require an active internet connection. Since the Wolfram|Alpha mobile app looks almost identical to WolframAlpha.com, and the website is better suited for several Pro capabilities like uploading data, this chapter will focus more on the look and feel of the website.

The first portion of this chapter will outline calculations that are available in both the free and Pro versions of Wolfram|Alpha, while the second portion of this chapter as well as subsequent chapters will outline calculations specific to the Pro version of Wolfram|Alpha. Readers with the Wolfram|Alpha Notebook Bundle can use the same login and password to access Wolfram|Alpha Pro and Wolfram|Alpha Notebook Edition.

In general, Wolfram|Alpha is useful for single calculations to support projects being created in other environments, especially since Wolfram|Alpha works well on secondary devices with small screens. Wolfram|Alpha Notebook Edition can perform similar calculations, but is useful as the primary environment for a project since it can contain series of calculations and support text and can act as the primary document for a project or provide supplemental materials for a course.

# Wolfram|Alpha Basics

Wolfram|Alpha has a straightforward interface for entering calculations. A single input field is used to enter calculations that can be stated in everyday English. Simple multiplication demonstrates how a calculation and result are formatted. After entering a calculation, the Enter key is used to perform the calculation and display the result.

Wolfram|Alpha results are formatted into a series of pods, which include the desired result of the calculation as well as several other related results to provide additional perspective. The screenshot above shows only the first two pods, which contain a confirmation for how the calculation was interpreted as well as the primary result. The screenshot below shows additional pods containing a number line, the number name with pronunciation and the number length.

 A section of related queries is also displayed below the results for any calculation. These suggestions provide an interesting view into what is possible in Wolfram|Alpha for other calculations.

The various pods contained in a result are based on the context of the calculation, and different calculations will often generate a different set of pods containing different related results. Results can include different types of graphics or charts, different algebraic relationships, various geographic maps, linguistic properties of words, a grid of numbers or data, or a large variety of other types of information depending on the context of the calculation. Wolfram|Alpha allocates a reasonable amount of time to each calculation and displays the set of results that can be calculated in that time.

Wolfram|Alpha can accept a wide variety of calculations in the form of everyday English, and can intersperse a wide variety of curated datasets as needed for a calculation. Since calculations can span so many domains, Wolfram|Alpha often provides insight into the assumptions it is making when taking everyday English and converting that phrase into a form that can be computed. The user has the ability to confirm that the interpretation is the desired interpretation, or change the interpretation as needed. In the following calculation, the default assumption is a fraction, with a date being an alternate assumption.

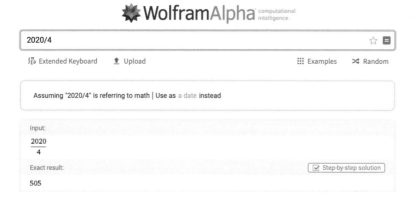

When a user clicks "a date" in the blue pod just below the calculation, Wolfram|Alpha changes its interpretation and displays results related to the date April 2020. The set of pods displayed in the results is completely different and provides a graphical display of a calendar, a time difference between the date in the calculation and the current date, observances for April 2020, phases of the Moon and other results related to that date.

Wolfram|Alpha provides exact answers when possible, so when the calculation is an irreducible fraction, the exact result is the same fraction with a notation stating that the fraction is irreducible. Another pod is provided automatically in the results with a decimal form.

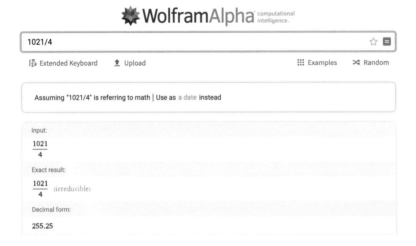

Calculations in Wolfram|Alpha are automated as much as possible, and in the previous result, Wolfram|Alpha provided an intuitive decimal form with two decimal places. Calculations can include additional phrasing to specify details manually rather than relying on this automation. Adding a phrase to specify a certain quantity of decimal places provides a different result.

 This overall idea applies to many types of calculations, and is especially useful to specify styling for a graph. The domain, range or coloring for a graph can be specified with intuitive phrasing.

In the previous calculation, the default decimal form is likely the desired form for the result. Other types of calculations might require clarification to achieve the desired result. For example, when calculating a decimal approximation of $\pi$, it is often useful to specify a quantity of decimal places, or even compare several calculations that vary the quantity of decimal places.

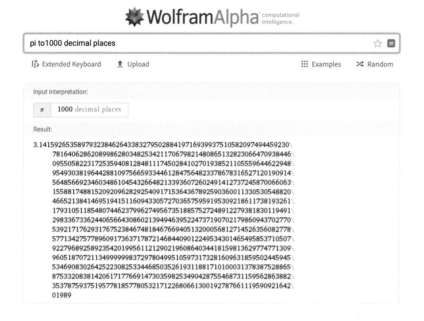

 Wolfram|Alpha has built-in knowledge on many special functions such as $\pi$, or units of measurement such as feet or miles. This built-in knowledge spans many different disciplines and courses.

So far in this chapter, the calculations have been specific, prompting Wolfram|Alpha to provide a specific result along with a collection of related results. It is also possible to enter very general calculations into Wolfram|Alpha, which provides a general collection of results. A general calculation could be an equation with no specific operation, a dataset with no specific operation or one or more real-world pieces of data with no specific query for that data.

The following calculation specifies only an equation with no operation on that equation, and Wolfram|Alpha provides many potentially useful results, including graphs, alternate forms, roots, a derivative, an indefinite integral, a global minimum, a definite integral and several other related results corresponding to the equation.

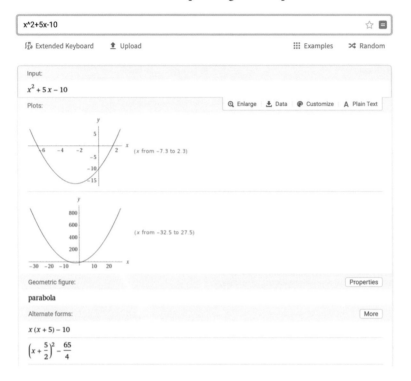

Later chapters will discuss how Wolfram|Alpha Notebook Edition can define a function and store a value of an equation so it can be used in a series of calculations. Wolfram|Alpha is designed for single calculations with predetermined results, while Wolfram|Alpha Notebook Edition makes it easier to document an idea through a progressive discussion on that topic.

When a calculation specifies only one piece of data, like a city, Wolfram|Alpha uses built-in knowledge to identify this term as a city and displays a collection of facts about that city. The input interpretation also shows Wolfram|Alpha contains data on sports teams, periodicals, music acts and movies in addition to cities.

The technology built into Wolfram|Alpha to understand everyday English and supply data is very sophisticated. A single calculation can use the word *apple* in multiple contexts: once in the context of the fruit, and once in the context of the company. The data can be queried and used in a live calculation.

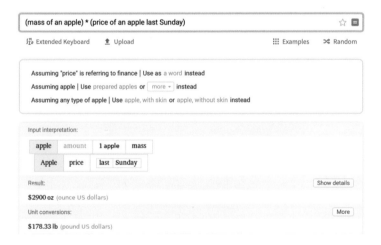

 The value of Apple stock will likely be different for the reader. The term "last Sunday" corresponds to the date when this chapter was written, and that stock price will almost certainly change over time.

# Wolfram|Alpha Pro Basics

## Keyboard Menu to Enter Typeset Characters

Describing symbols or calculations in everyday English often works well in Wolfram|Alpha, but Wolfram|Alpha Pro contains a keyboard with typeset characters that can be used in calculations. Symbols like $\pi$ and $\infty$ are available, as well as symbols to perform calculations like indefinite integration, summation or partial derivatives using notation that is commonly found in a textbook.

The set of symbols appears after clicking the **Extended Keyboard** button just below the main input field for calculations. When clicking any of the buttons, that symbol is inserted at the position of the cursor in the calculation.

Symbols can be used to enter an indefinite integral that includes a square root. The set of pods displayed in the result confirms Wolfram|Alpha understands these symbols, and returns the solution along with several graphical visualizations.

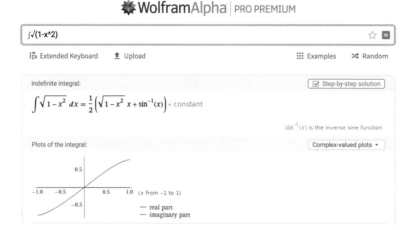

## Step-by-Step Solutions

While the primary result for a mathematical calculation in Wolfram|Alpha contains only the final solution, Wolfram|Alpha Pro contains a sophisticated set of solvers to display step-by-step solutions for many of the problems in precollege- or college-level mathematics.

Much of the functionality for step-by-step solutions is related to mathematics, but step-by-step solutions are also available for other areas, like balancing chemical equations or calculating physics problems using specific formulas.

A previous calculation in this chapter involving an indefinite integral is one example where Wolfram|Alpha Pro can display a step-by-step solution. After clicking this **Step-by-step solution** button, a new set of pods is displayed representing the major steps in solving this problem.

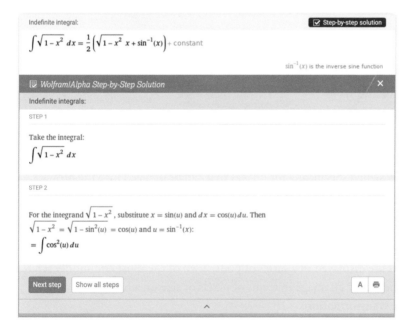

The steps of the solution can be shown one at a time to act as a real-time quiz for the user, or the steps can be shown all at once to aid in double-checking a solution.

Step-by-step solutions are very useful throughout many mathematics or science courses, and since this is such a commonly used aspect of Wolfram|Alpha Pro, a later chapter will outline step-by-step solutions in much more detail.

Step-by-step solutions are also available in Wolfram|Alpha Notebook Edition, and later chapters will show how to use step-by-step solutions in a series of other calculations or graphics to gain insight into a course concept.

## Upload Images or Data

In addition to the **Extended Keyboard** button, Wolfram|Alpha Pro also includes a button to upload images or data from a user's machine to Wolfram|Alpha Pro for analysis. This menu for uploading external files can be accessed by clicking the **Upload** button located just to the right of the **Extended Keyboard** button in Wolfram|Alpha Pro.

The first choice is designed specifically for images that can be dragged into the browser menu, entered with a URL if the image is stored on a website or chosen within the file structure of the user's local machine after clicking the **Click, Drag, or Tap** button.

After choosing the image and pressing Enter to run the default set of calculations on the image, many results are displayed in a series of pods. Two of the most commonly referenced results are the size of an image in terms of pixels or size on a hard drive, and a collection of image transformations.

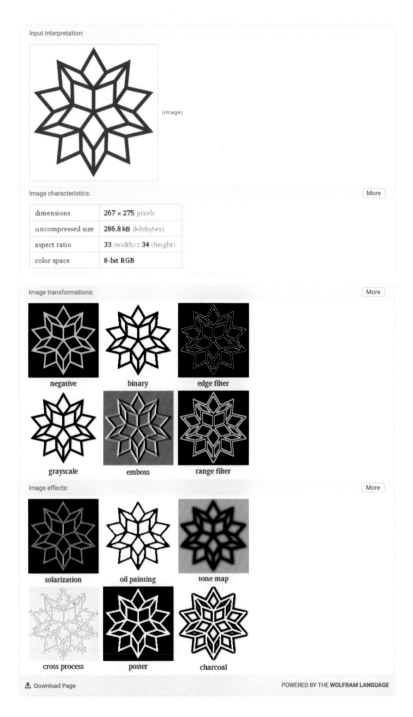

In addition to image files, spreadsheet files can be uploaded to Wolfram|Alpha Pro, and several charts and statistics tests are displayed in the results to gain understanding of the dataset. The **File Upload** tab is the third choice after clicking the **Upload** button, and the same type of **Click, Drag, or Tap** interface is provided for both a spreadsheet file and an image file.

At the time of this book's publication, Wolfram|Alpha Pro provides a more stream-lined way to upload an external spreadsheet file compared to Wolfram|Alpha Notebook Edition. A later chapter will discuss downloading charts or results that can then be used in Wolfram|Alpha Notebook Edition.

Uploading a CSV file with 10 values creates a set of pods in the result, including a summary of the data; a list plot of the raw data; a histogram of values; min and max values; and several statistics tests like mean, standard deviation and median.

Similar to step-by-step solutions, uploading data is another very common use of Wolfram|Alpha Pro, and a later chapter will outline more examples based on several different types of datasets in more detail.

While this chapter outlines the most commonly used aspects of Wolfram|Alpha Pro, this is not a complete list of functionality. Wolfram Problem Generator, viewing a history of calculations or use of Wolfram|Alpha Pro through a mobile app are all aspects of Wolfram|Alpha Pro that are not outlined in this book. The WolframAlpha.com website contains more examples on all capabilities in Wolfram|Alpha Pro.

# Conclusion

Wolfram|Alpha and Wolfram|Alpha Pro are commonly used to support projects or coursework since Wolfram|Alpha can be accessed on a wide variety of devices. Quickly performing calculations, generating graphics, viewing step-by-step solutions and generating a statistical analysis of an external dataset on a tablet or phone or in web browser can be a useful supplement to a project or course.

# Exercises

These are all simple exercises that will need to be completed at WolframAlpha.com:

1. Calculate how many meters are in a mile.

2. Find the list of the five heaviest elements in the periodic table.

3. Find out how much calcium is in one cup of mozzarella cheese.

4. Calculate the area of a triangle with sides 5, 12 and 13.

5. Calculate the total length of all roads in Spain.

6. Find the list of famous people born on January 17, 1922.

7. What was the high temperature in Chicago on July 4, 1976?

8. What is the population difference of Tokyo and London?

9. How many marbles can fit into a box measuring 10 cubic inches?

10. Find all the words that match the pattern _al_d.

# Step-by-Step Solutions in Wolfram|Alpha Pro

## Introduction

Step-by-step solutions in Wolfram|Alpha Pro are available for a variety of problems throughout a wide variety of courses, making this aspect of Wolfram|Alpha Pro very popular for students or learners. In some cases, step-by-step solutions are useful for confirming understanding of a current course topic, while in other cases step-by-step solutions are useful for reviewing concepts from a previous course as a refresher for those topics.

## Arithmetic and Algebra

Previous chapters have outlined Wolfram|Alpha's ability to calculate results formatted in a series of pods, which include the primary result as well as several related results. Step-by-step solutions are also a type of pod in Wolfram|Alpha Pro, with uniform styling for any supported type of solution. If a step-by-step solution is available, the button to display that solution is always located to the right of the primary result.

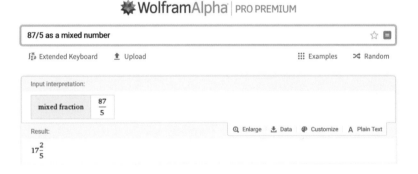

Initially, after clicking the **Step-by-step solution** button, a new pod is inserted just below the result to display the first step of the step-by-step solution. This new pod provides two main choices to access the step-by-step solution. The first choice is to scroll through the steps one by one using the **Next step** button. This allows the user to concentrate on each step either to verify a solution that has been calculated by hand or to practice and gain an intuitive feel for the major steps to solve a particular problem by hand.

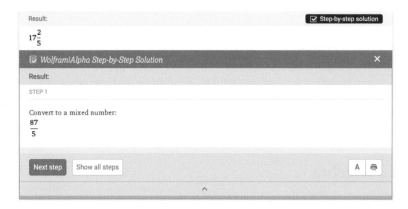

When working through the steps one at a time, Wolfram|Alpha Pro provides a hint after clicking the **Next step** button so the user can pause to compare their conceptual approach to the problem with the hint in the step-by-step solution.

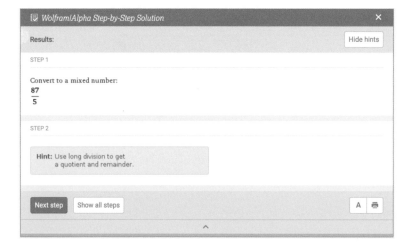

Clicking the **Next step** button a second time displays the implementation of the concept in the hint. In this case, step 2 sets up a long division problem.

Clicking the **Next step** button a third and fourth time displays the hint for step 3, as well as the calculation corresponding to step 3. For this problem, an intermediate step is included related to the arithmetic of dividing 8 by 5, and this intermediate step can be displayed by clicking the plus icon at the lower right of the solution to that step.

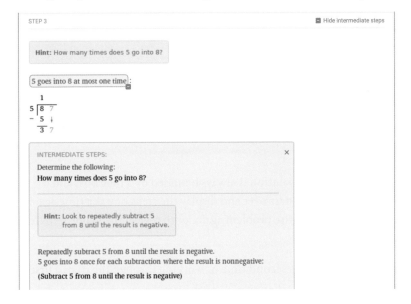

It is important to note that Wolfram|Alpha is not displaying results based on a database of problems. The technology identifies the type of problem, then provides live computation to solve the problem, so a very wide scope of problems can be solved with step-by-step solutions.

The **Next step** button can be clicked to continue through the steps until Wolfram|Alpha Pro displays the final answer. For this problem, there are six steps, two of which include optional intermediate steps.

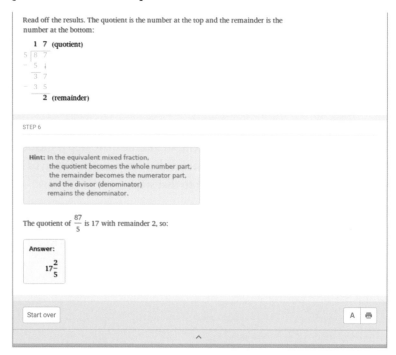

The final answer for any step-by-step solution is always bounded by a blue box, and a button is displayed with an option to start over and display the steps one at a time again. This allows the user to practice the entire problem again, or to review the major steps for solving the problem again.

Whether a user is reviewing the steps a second time or working through the steps a first time, the **Hide hints** button eliminates that portion of the step-by-step solution and shows only the specific steps of the solution. This view is useful when checking a manually created solution side by side with the steps in Wolfram|Alpha Pro.

The second main choice to access the step-by-step solutions is to click the **Show all steps** button, which can be clicked at any point and displays all the steps at once. For users comparing a manually created solution to the steps in Wolfram|Alpha Pro, this can also be the most efficient way to check several problems in a row, along with hiding the hints.

So far in this chapter, a step-by-step solution has been outlined using an arithmetic problem, but the same buttons are displayed to work through a step-by-step solution for any supported problem. After switching the calculation to an algebra problem, the same **Step-by-step solution** button is displayed to the right of the primary result, and the **Next step** and **Show all steps** buttons are displayed to navigate through the step-by-step solution.

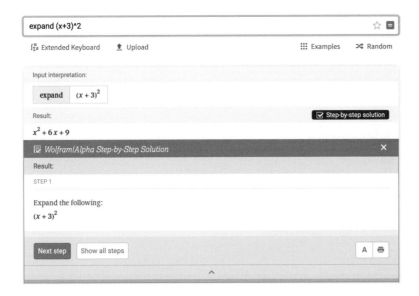

While the buttons to advance through the solution are the same, the steps themselves are much different for an algebra problem compared to an arithmetic problem. In this case, Wolfram|Alpha Pro recognizes the FOIL (first, outer, inner, last) method as the best solution for this type of problem and applies that in the second step.

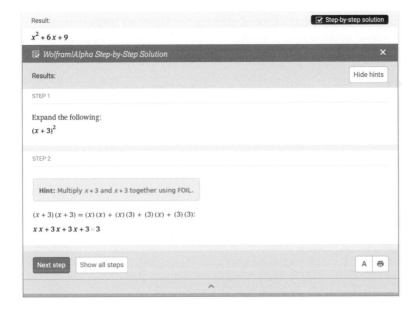

As mentioned earlier in the chapter, Wolfram|Alpha Pro is not using a database of problems to provide step-by-step solutions. The technology identifies the type of problem and performs live calculations to generate the step-by-step solution.

Since the same input field is used to start any calculation and Wolfram|Alpha Pro automatically recognizes the most appropriate step-by-step solution, a user does not need to first identify how to solve a problem, or how a problem might fit into a particular course or education level to use the step-by-step solutions in Wolfram|Alpha Pro. This means step-by-step solutions are useful not just to outline the steps to solve a specific problem, but are also useful to tutor a student on what methodology is best to solve the problem.

 This is especially useful in cases when a learner is reviewing materials and does not remember what specific course materials are most relevant to review how to solve that particular type of problem.

The rest of the steps to calculate the solution can be displayed either by clicking the **Next step** button to display the steps one at a time or clicking the **Show all steps** button to display all remaining steps in the solution. In this case, five steps are used to solve the problem, one of which includes an optional intermediate step.

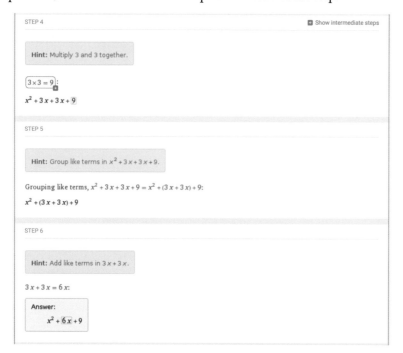

After the final answer, which is bounded by the same blue box, is displayed, the same choice to start over and work through the solution again is shown. The same choice to hide the hints is also available at any point.

## Calculus, Chemistry and Other Areas

Step-by-step solutions are very popular to support precollege- or college-level calculus courses since Wolfram|Alpha Pro can identify the appropriate solution to mirror how a textbook solves a particular problem. Since results to calculations as well as the step-by-step solutions are live calculations, Wolfram|Alpha Pro can help with sophisticated problems that are time-consuming to solve by hand.

So far in this chapter, a typical variable name $x$ has been used for an algebraic calculation, but Wolfram|Alpha Pro can also solve problems where coefficients are also symbols to provide general solutions to problems.

The following calculation uses the symbols $a$, $b$, $c$ and $d$ and calculates a derivative with respect to $x$. The primary result is given in terms of the symbols $a$, $b$, $c$ and $d$, and the step-by-step solution supports this type of symbolic expression as well.

 The phrase "with respect to x" can actually be left out of this calculation since $x$ is such a commonly used variable for these types of problems. Wolfram|Alpha Pro will assume $x$ is the variable of interest.

Just as the FOIL method is identified as the best approach for expanding an algebraic expression in the previous calculation, Wolfram|Alpha Pro identifies the quotient rule as the best approach to calculate this derivative.

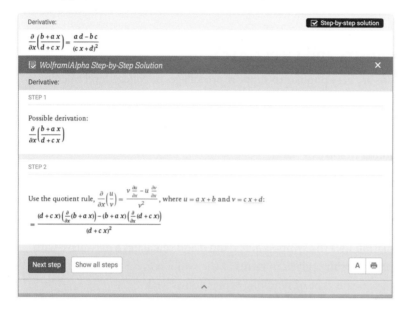

The step-by-step solution includes 11 steps with four optional intermediate steps to solve the problem, and again, the same buttons can be used to advance to the next step or show all steps at once.

In calculus, the best approach to solve a problem often depends on the form of the equation in the calculation. Wolfram|Alpha Pro identified the quotient rule as the best method to solve the previous problem, and in the following calculation, Wolfram|Alpha Pro identifies the chain rule as the best method to solve this problem based on the form of the equation.

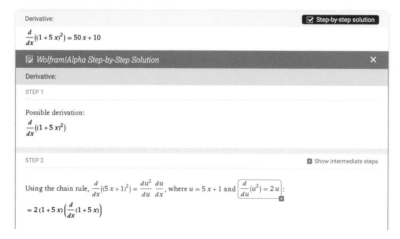

For other calculations involving derivatives, the product rule might be a useful starting point in a step-by-step solution to solve the problem.

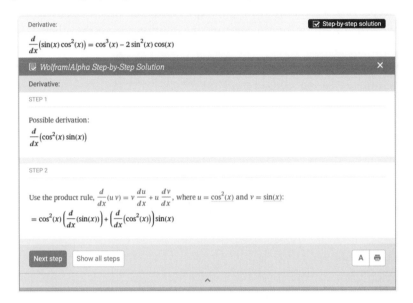

For certain problems, Wolfram|Alpha Pro might recognize multiple ways to solve a particular problem, and in those cases, it provides a drop-down menu to the left of the **Hide hints** button to allow the user to choose the method used for the step-by-step solution. In the following calculation, a formula can be used, or a gradient can be used to find a tangent plane to a surface at a certain point.

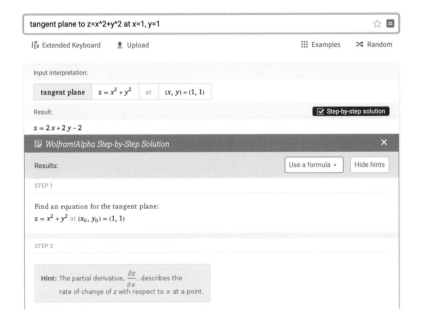

Toggling to the **Use the gradient** solution changes the steps and solves the problem based on this different method. In this case, using the gradient provides a solution with five steps, while using a formula provides a solution with eight steps. A user can choose the desired methodology to review their solution, or can compare one solution against the other.

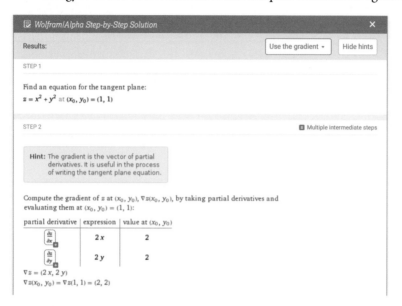

The previous examples span introductory calculus through more advanced multi-variable calculus, but the overall concept is applicable to most courses. There are many problems where multiple methods are available to solve a problem, and the desired approach can be chosen by the user.

So far in this chapter, step-by-step solutions have been used to solve problems in several different levels of mathematics, but step-by-step solutions are available for other areas of science as well. Balancing chemical equations is a common use of step-by-step solutions outside of mathematics.

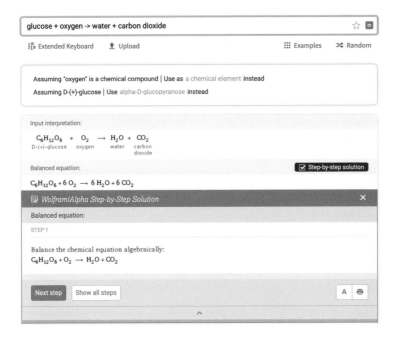

Since Wolfram|Alpha includes extensive knowledge of chemicals, the common name can be used to enter the names of chemical compounds, and Wolfram|Alpha Pro will show the chemical equation throughout the process of balancing the equation.

A calculation to balance a chemical equation can also use chemical formulas. In either case, the **Input interpretation** pod can be used to confirm Wolfram|Alpha is using the desired chemical compounds when balancing the equation. The step-by-step solution to balance a chemical equation based on common names is identical to the step-by-step solution based on chemical formulas. Five steps are outlined in the step-by-step solution describing the chemistry concepts to balance the equation for either case.

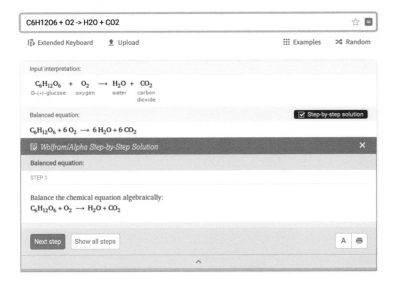

# Conclusion

Step-by-step solutions in Wolfram|Alpha Pro span many courses and fields, making it useful in many classes in an educational program. Wolfram|Alpha Pro can act as a real-time tutor to help identify whether a solution is correct, or where a solution might deviate from the correct solution. Also, step-by-step solutions are a valuable tool to refresh an understanding of concepts from previous courses or areas where a learner has less experience.

# Exercises

These are all simple exercises that will need to be done at WolframAlpha.com (and a Pro account is required to get the additional features like step-by-step solutions).

1. Find the average of $(1, 2, 3, 4, 5, 6, 7)$, and generate the step-by-step solution.

2. What is the probability of rolling 7, 8 or 9 using two fair six-sided dice? Generate the step-by-step solution.

3. Find the solutions for $x^2 + 5x + 6 = 0$, and generate the step-by-step solution.

4. Calculate the area of a circle with radius 2, and generate the step-by-step solution.

5. Calculate the distance between the points (3, 2) and (5, 1), and generate the step-by-step solution.

6. Determine if 81 is a prime number, and generate the step-by-step solution.

7. Display the Lewis structure of $NO_2$, and generate the step-by-step solution.

8. Balance the equation glucose + oxygen -> water + carbon dioxide, and generate the step-by-step solution.

9. Find the determinant of the matrix ((1, 2, 1), (1, 1, 0), (0, 1, 1)), and generate the step-by-step solution.

10. Compute the cross-product of (1, 2, 3) × (3, 4, 5), and generate the step-by-step solution.

# CHAPTER 5

# Using Your Own Data in Wolfram|Alpha Pro

## Introduction

A previous chapter outlined the basics of uploading an external file to Wolfram|Alpha Pro and showed common calculations that are automatically performed to display various charts and statistics tests. This chapter will show a wider variety of possible calculations based on different types of external data files, each with a different structure, and will show common ways to download results so charts can be used in a project or supplemental materials for a course.

## Uploading Datasets with a Single Number

Although Wolfram|Alpha Pro is commonly used to solve problems in mathematics involving equations, calculations involving a list of numbers provide a completely different set of results and can be equally useful. When entering a calculation involving a dataset of single numbers, it is often easiest to type the numbers manually, using parentheses to represent the list of numbers. While a specific operation could be specified in the calculation, like creating a graph or calculating an average of a dataset, it is common to enter a dataset with no operation in the calculation. Wolfram|Alpha will often create a very useful collection of graphs and statistics tests that includes the desired result as well as other calculations of interest.

The result for the following calculation is a graph in the form of a number line, a pie chart and several statistical tests like mean, median and standard deviation.

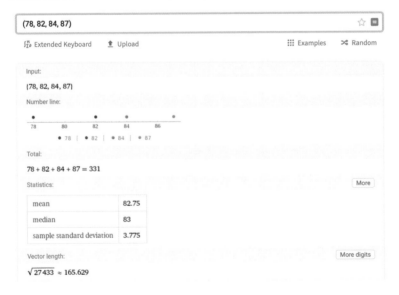

While a pie chart is included in the results for the previous calculation, a bar chart is not displayed. A more specific calculation can specify a bar chart if that is the desired result.

The values in the calculations above are integers, but a decimal with any quantity of decimal places can be used instead in a dataset.

While this method of creating calculations is often very useful for modest-sized datasets, Wolfram|Alpha Pro supports uploading spreadsheet files, which can be a much more efficient way to create charts and calculations for larger datasets compared to retyping the data into a calculation.

If a spreadsheet contains a list of single numbers, separated by rows and all in the same column, this file will be interpreted as a list of single values when uploaded to Wolfram|Alpha Pro.

| | A | B | C | D |
|---|---|---|---|---|
| 1 | 78 | | | |
| 2 | 82 | | | |
| 3 | 84 | | | |
| 4 | 87 | | | |
| 5 | 84 | | | |
| 6 | 91 | | | |
| 7 | 90 | | | |
| 8 | 95 | | | |
| 9 | 89 | | | |
| 10 | 90 | | | |
| 11 | | | | |
| 12 | | | | |

To upload this external file to Wolfram|Alpha Pro, the **File Upload** tab can be used after clicking the **Upload** button to either drag and drop the file from the desktop to Wolfram|Alpha Pro or to choose the file using the file structure of the local computer. Once the file is selected, it will be represented in the input field using the file name, and is bounded by an orange box.

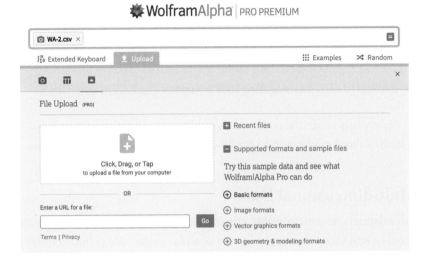

Similar to the first calculation in this chapter, pressing Enter to start the calculation without any specific operation will return a collection of results including charts and statistics.

The **Input interpretation** pod confirms Wolfram|Alpha Pro's understanding that the CSV file contains 10 elements and the **Underlying data** pod shows the 10 items. Since the values are single numbers, a graph of the raw data is the next result in the collection of results, with options to change the scale of the $y$ axis and the style for joining the points on the graph.

The **Underlying data** pod also includes a button to sort the dataset. Original order is displayed by default, but sorting can be a useful way to spot data points that have been accidentally duplicated without navigating back to separate spreadsheet software.

Since this dataset is slightly larger than the one in the first calculation of this chapter, a histogram is included in the collection of results to graphically show commonality in the values.

## Uploading Multidimensional Data

When each value in a dataset contains multiple values, this can be described as multidimensional data. In some datasets, each value might consist of an $(x, y)$ pair where both values are numbers. In other datasets, a subset of the values might be words or other non-numeric values. Wolfram|Alpha Pro can accept external files with either format, and automatically recognizes when non-numeric data is included in the dataset.

The following multidimensional dataset contains text in column A and numeric values in column B.

| | A | B | C | D |
|---|---|---|---|---|
| 1 | Test 1 | 78 | | |
| 2 | Test 1 | 82 | | |
| 3 | Test 1 | 84 | | |
| 4 | Test 1 | 87 | | |
| 5 | Test 1 | 84 | | |
| 6 | Test 2 | 91 | | |
| 7 | Test 2 | 90 | | |
| 8 | Test 2 | 95 | | |
| 9 | Test 2 | 89 | | |
| 10 | Test 2 | 90 | | |
| 11 | | | | |
| 12 | | | | |

The same process can be used to upload this new dataset into Wolfram|Alpha Pro by clicking the **Click, Drag, or Tap** button located in the **File Upload** tab, which users can access by clicking the **Upload** button. The **Input interpretation** pod confirms Wolfram|Alpha Pro's understanding that the dataset contains two columns and 10 rows. The **Underlying data** preview displays the raw data in a grid using the labels "column 1" and "column 2," similar to viewing the data in external spreadsheet software.

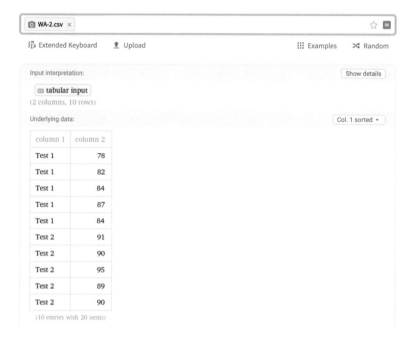

 While Wolfram|Alpha Pro is very useful for charts and statistics, it does not contain a way to scrub the data and change values in the grid above. It is good practice to perform final edits in spreadsheet software, then upload the data.

In addition to displaying a straightforward chart of the raw data in column 2, Wolfram|Alpha Pro displays more sophisticated charts to show the numeric values in column 2 based on the textual information in column 1. A histogram is included to graphically display commonality in the values, with different colors for the labels "Test 1" and "Test 2" from column 1. Pie charts are also displayed to count the quantity of data points corresponding to Test 1 and Test 2, or to tally the data points corresponding to Test 1 and Test 2.

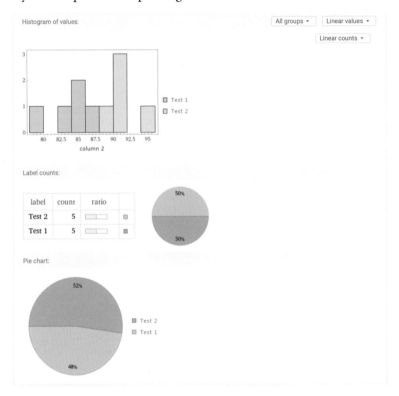

Wolfram|Alpha Pro can create a wide variety of charts and calculations, and the collection of results for multidimensional data is longer than the collection of results for a dataset with single values. In addition to multiple charts and statistical tests, Wolfram|Alpha Pro also tries to automatically draw conclusions from the data. In this case, a statistical statement is included confirming Test 1 and Test 2 have significantly different medians, and a regression analysis shows column 2 has no statistically significant effect on column 1.

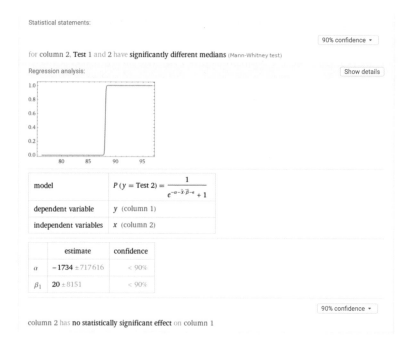

Statistical statements:

90% confidence ▾

for column 2, Test 1 and 2 have **significantly different medians** (Mann-Whitney test)

Regression analysis:

Show details

| | | |
|---|---|---|
| model | $P\,(y = \text{Test 2}) = \dfrac{1}{e^{-a - \hat{x}\,\hat{\beta} - \epsilon} + 1}$ | |
| dependent variable | $y$ (column 1) | |
| independent variables | $x$ (column 2) | |

| | estimate | confidence |
|---|---|---|
| $a$ | $-1734 \pm 717616$ | < 90% |
| $\beta_1$ | $20 \pm 8151$ | < 90% |

90% confidence ▾

column 2 has **no statistically significant effect** on column 1

Notice Wolfram|Alpha Pro's built-in knowledge includes formulas related to statistical tests. Wolfram|Alpha's built-in knowledge also includes formulas in many areas, including physical science, life science, business, mathematics and several other areas.

So far in this section, Wolfram|Alpha Pro has identified two common phrases in column 1 and created charts and statistical conclusions based on those two common phrases. When using a different external file with three common phrases in column 1, Wolfram|Alpha Pro recognizes the third phrase and updates the charts and statistical tests to include three groups of values.

In spreadsheet form, the dataset still contains two columns, but now includes rows for Test 3 in addition to Test 1 and Test 2.

| | A | B | C | D |
|---|---|---|---|---|
| 1 | Test 1 | 78 | | |
| 2 | Test 1 | 82 | | |
| 3 | Test 1 | 84 | | |
| 4 | Test 1 | 87 | | |
| 5 | Test 1 | 84 | | |
| 6 | Test 2 | 91 | | |
| 7 | Test 2 | 90 | | |
| 8 | Test 2 | 95 | | |
| 9 | Test 2 | 89 | | |
| 10 | Test 2 | 90 | | |
| 11 | Test 3 | 68 | | |
| 12 | Test 3 | 67 | | |
| 13 | Test 3 | 69 | | |
| 14 | Test 3 | 67 | | |
| 15 | Test 3 | 72 | | |
| 16 | | | | |

How large of a file is supported for Wolfram|Alpha Pro? The limitation is sometimes the available computation time on Wolfram servers, but Wolfram|Alpha Pro supports files up to 2 MB, which should be suitable for course examples.

After uploading this new CSV file, Wolfram|Alpha Pro displays a collection of the same charts compared to the previous CSV file, and the graph of raw data includes the larger quantity of values. The histogram and pie charts, however, now use three colors to distinguish the values in Test 1, Test 2 and Test 3.

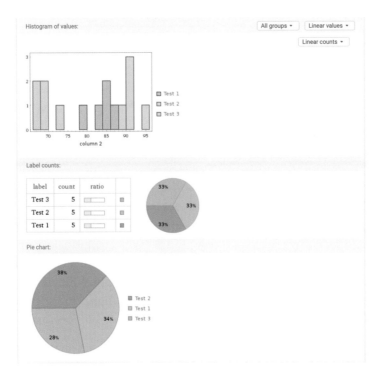

The statistical statements are expanded to show Tests 1, 2 and 3 have significantly different medians, and a new chart of aggregate properties by label is created to visualize totals, medians, counts and distributions for each of the tests. Properties for all labels in column 1 are also displayed.

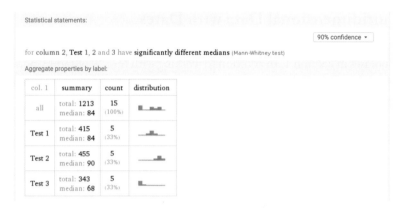

A one-way ANOVA and a box-and-whisker chart are also created.

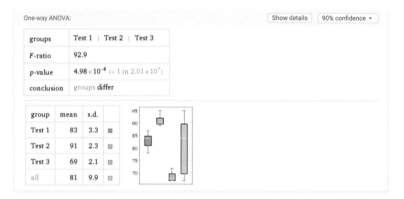

 Several types of charts or calculations can be adjusted to include different assumptions or styling. For example, in the charts above, the styling can be changed to a log scale instead of a linear scale, or the confidence level can be changed for the one-way ANOVA test.

# Uploading Multidimensional Data with Dates

So far in this chapter, Wolfram|Alpha Pro has grouped different numerical values according to common textual phrases in column 1. In addition to working with text, Wolfram|Alpha Pro can also recognize values that represent dates. The following dataset adds a third column that includes various date values.

| | A | B | C | D |
|---|---|---|---|---|
| 1 | Test 1 | 78 | 2-Feb-18 | |
| 2 | Test 1 | 82 | 3-Feb-18 | |
| 3 | Test 1 | 84 | 2-Feb-18 | |
| 4 | Test 1 | 87 | 4-Feb-18 | |
| 5 | Test 1 | 84 | 4-Feb-18 | |
| 6 | Test 2 | 91 | 15-Mar-18 | |
| 7 | Test 2 | 90 | 14-Mar-18 | |
| 8 | Test 2 | 95 | 16-Mar-18 | |
| 9 | Test 2 | 89 | 14-Mar-18 | |
| 10 | Test 2 | 90 | 14-Mar-18 | |
| 11 | Test 3 | 68 | 2-Apr-18 | |
| 12 | Test 3 | 67 | 3-Apr-18 | |
| 13 | Test 3 | 69 | 2-Apr-18 | |
| 14 | Test 3 | 67 | 2-Apr-18 | |
| 15 | Test 3 | 72 | 2-Apr-18 | |
| 16 | | | | |

After uploading this new dataset and performing the default calculation without any option, many of the same charts and statistical tests are displayed, since the first two columns of data are identical to the previous dataset. However, several of the results include a drop-down menu to specify all data or refine the calculation to a subset of the data based on common phrases in column 1. The statistics tests for mean, standard deviation, min, median and a variety of other values can be displayed for all data, or just data corresponding to Test 1, Test 2 or Test 3.

In addition to more drop-down menus, a few additional charts are displayed based on the data in column 3 corresponding to the new date values. The chart above shows binned totals of values in column 2 based on days of the week, with additional coloring to show values related to the unique phrases in column 1. This chart provides a unique perspective based on all three columns.

This chart is a good example of Wolfram|Alpha Pro's ability to show patterns that would otherwise be difficult to identify, especially through visual inspection in spreadsheet software. For example, Friday is the only day of the week with values corresponding to both Test 1 and Test 2, which could lead to unique insights in the dataset.

## Downloading Data

In a previous chapter, Wolfram|Alpha Pro was used to restyle an image with a variety of filters, and the results were returned as a grid of images. To use one of the filtered images in another application, Wolfram|Alpha Pro also provides a way to download images or data.

The charts created by Wolfram|Alpha Pro based on spreadsheet data can also be downloaded as external files, and this chapter will also outline that process.

Each pod within a collection of results includes a **Data Download** button that is displayed in the lower-right-hand corner when hovering over that pod with a mouse.

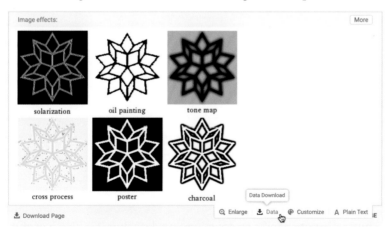

Clicking the **Data Download** button creates a new pod with several options to specify the format for the file that will be downloaded to the user's local machine. Image formats are the most common, and BMP, GIF, JPEG and PNG are available formats for downloading the filtered images under the **Raster Graphics** tab.

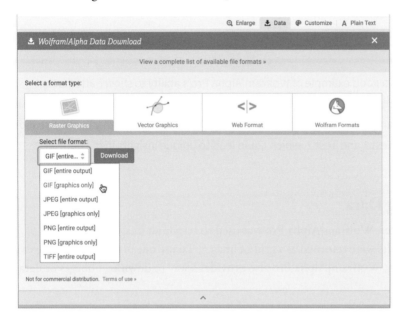

In addition to downloading filtered images, any of the charts created by Wolfram|Alpha Pro based on an uploaded spreadsheet file can also be downloaded in image format. These pods also contain a **Data Download** button in the lower-right corner of the pod that is displayed when mousing over the pod.

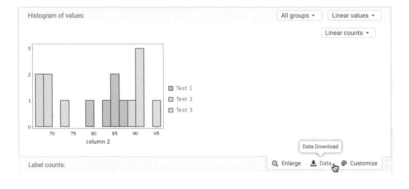

 The **Enlarge** button is not specific to downloading data, but it is also a useful way to increase the size of charts within Wolfram|Alpha Pro to more easily see details in the charts.

In general, a chart is typically used in a wider variety of applications compared to a filtered image. The first tab for raster graphics contains many types of image formats, including BMP or other larger file formats, which are useful for downloading an image of a chart. In addition to the choices in the first tab, the second tab includes several vector graphics formats, including PDF or EPS, which are commonly used for publications. The third tab includes many of the same choices as **Raster Graphics**, but refines the list to only image formats with a modest file size, which work well when posting the image to a website. The fourth tab includes CDF and NB formats to open the graphic in Wolfram|Alpha Notebook Edition or other Wolfram products. Even if the chart is downloaded as an image, it can be inserted into Wolfram|Alpha Notebook Edition for use in projects or coursework, and other chapters outline the process to accomplish this.

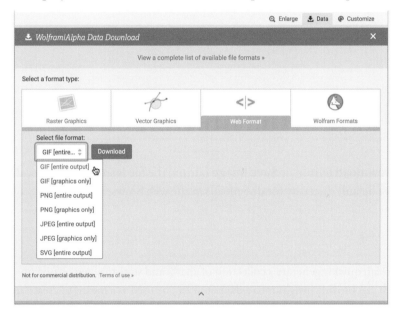

In addition to downloading a chart with the default styling, the **Customize** button next to the **Data Download** button can be used to change the styling of a chart. This includes changing the coloring of a chart, specifying whether a title or frame should be included in the downloaded image, increasing or decreasing the size of the downloaded image and choosing a file format. Experimenting with the size of the downloaded image is often useful when using that image in another application or on a website to make sure the image is displayed with the desired clarity.

After clicking the **Download** button or **Save Image** button, the file is stored on the local machine in the user's default directory for downloads in the web browser.

## Conclusion

Wolfram|Alpha Pro can quickly generate a collection of charts and statistical tests based on uploaded data, which can provide insight into a dataset or can be used as a means to create and download charts for use in another application. The knowledge built into Wolfram|Alpha Pro and the technology for storing and handling data are very useful for user-defined datasets, even when the dataset contains a mix of numeric values, text and date values.

## Exercises

1. Open a web browser and type in the following URL:
   https://www.handsonstart.com/WA-7.csv
   Choose **Save File** to save a copy of the CSV file to the local machine.

2. Navigate to WolframAlpha.com and upload the data file from Exercise 1.

3. Within the collection of results from Exercise 2, show the details of the input interpretation to view which columns are numeric, versus a location, versus a date.

4. Within the collection of results from Exercise 2, change the underlying data preview to be increasing based on column 2.

5. Within the collection of results from Exercise 2, show all the items for the underlying data.

6. Within the collection of results from Exercise 2, customize the plot to include a frame, a title, a large image size, and then download the image in JPEG format.

7. Within the collection of results from Exercise 2, download the data for the pie chart, choose the list of vector graphics formats, and download the image in PDF format.

8. Within the collection of results from Exercise 2, display more results under the Statistics pod to display sample standard deviation and sample variance.

9. Within the collection of results from Exercise 2, display the statistical measures for only Detroit, Michigan.

10. Within the collection of results from Exercise 2, display the statistical measures for only Omaha, Nebraska.

# The Very Basics of Wolfram|Alpha Notebook Edition

## Introduction

Since Wolfram|Alpha Notebook Edition provides a useful workflow for calculations using everyday English, a new user can perform calculations almost immediately. Many people learn by doing, and this chapter is designed to be used as practice to create a variety of calculations and gain experience. Readers often have the software and the book side by side so each input in the chapter can be typed into Wolfram|Alpha Notebook Edition.

This chapter will briefly explain how to get started when a user first launches the software, then will provide several examples to retype to gain experience with the software. Subsequent chapters will include more detail on the scope of functionality as well as provide more examples that are useful in a particular course or field.

## Launching a Notebook

Wolfram|Alpha Notebook Edition documents can contain a mix of calculations, text, graphics and animations, and these documents are called notebooks. This chapter will provide experience with entering and evaluating some introductory calculations. After launching the software, a welcome screen is displayed that requires a user to log in to the software. This welcome screen has links to quick tips, which are a nice supplement to this book, along with a link to the Wolfram|Alpha website, which is a related technology that has been outlined in previous chapters.

 Keep in mind an internet connection is required to log in as well as perform calculations in the software.

To launch a notebook, click the **New Document** button on the welcome screen, and a new blank notebook will appear instead of the welcome screen.

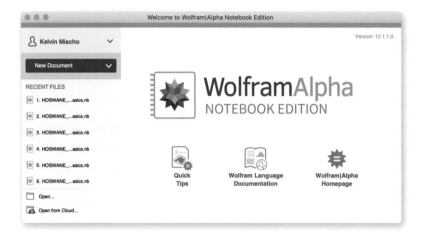

 It is possible to view multiple notebooks on a computer screen or create several notebooks in the software. Clicking the **File** drop-down menu and choosing **New** then **Notebook** creates a new notebook and does not replace any currently opened notebooks.

All new notebooks are blank documents, and include one blank input cell that can be used for a first calculation. The term "cell" is used to denote various content in a notebook. Each cell has blue cell marker on the right of the screen, and a notebook is just a collection of many cells. This concept will be explained in more detail in subsequent chapters.

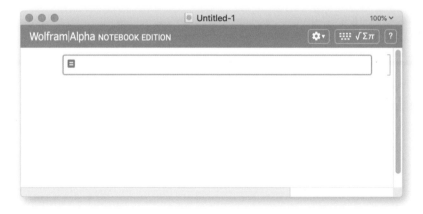

# Basic Calculations

To enter a first calculation, type "10!" into the blank input cell, then press the Enter key to evaluate this calculation.

3 628 800

After evaluation, several cells are automatically created, which will be discussed in more detail in subsequent chapters. The final cell is called an output cell and contains the result of the calculation, whether that is simple arithmetic, a symbolic calculation involving equations or a calculation that generates graphics.

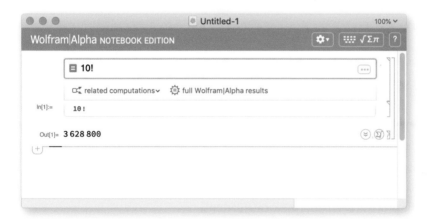

After a calculation is performed, a horizontal bar will also appear. This horizontal bar marks the position at which to add a new calculation. By default, the bar is positioned just below the previous result, but it is also possible to click anywhere in a notebook to insert new calculations above or between other existing calculations. This chapter will follow an easy pattern of adding new calculations below the previous calculation, and other chapters will outline how to add various content into notebooks in more detail.

A second calculation can be created just by typing; the new orange-bounded formatting will be created automatically. Type "717/3" to start a second calculation to perform simple division.

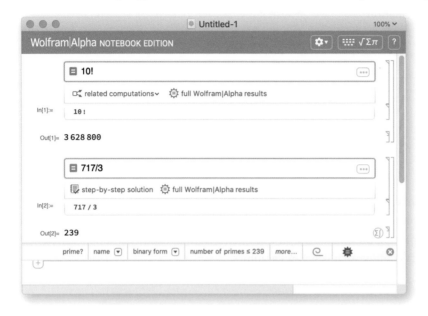

After this second calculation, the notebook now contains two input cells along with two output cells for the results for each calculation.

 For readers performing calculations in Wolfram|Alpha Notebook Edition for the first time, it is sometimes easier to get started by watching a video of someone typing the calculations. This video (wolfr.am/hostwane) starts with a blank notebook and shows the process of creating new calculations.

Next, create a third calculation to divide 718 by 3. By default, the result will be an exact value.

$$\frac{718}{3}$$

The following calculation approximates the same fraction to five digits.

718/3 to 5 digits

N[718/3, 5]

239.33

---

 Again, for each new calculation the reader can just begin typing, and the orange-bounded formatting will appear for the next calculation. This chapter will continue with examples, and the reader's version of the notebook will grow into a nice collection of examples as they type along.

To create a variable, use the term "set" to assign a value of 5 to the symbol *a*.

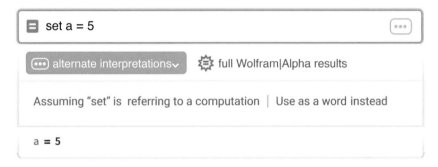

set a = 5

alternate interpretations⌄    full Wolfram|Alpha results

Assuming "set" is referring to a computation | Use as a word instead

a = 5

5

Now that the symbol *a* contains a stored value, any subsequent calculations will replace the symbol *a* with the stored value of 5.

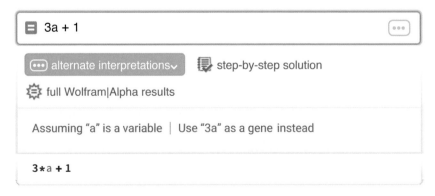

3a + 1

alternate interpretations⌄    step-by-step solution

full Wolfram|Alpha results

Assuming "a" is a variable | Use "3a" as a gene instead

3*a + 1

16

Use the term "unset" to clear the stored value from the symbol *a*.

⊟ unset a  ⋯

> Clear[a]

The term "unset" is one of several possible phrases to clear a variable. The term "clear" works identically. It is also possible to keep the notebook open in the software but close the computation engine that runs in the background by clicking the **Evaluation** menu and choosing **Quit Kernel**. This will clear all stored values for any symbol.

Now that the symbol *a* has no stored value, expand an algebraic expression using the symbol *a*, which now acts as a variable.

⊟ expand (a + 5)(a + 9)  ⋯

📑 step-by-step solution    🌟 full Wolfram|Alpha results

> Expand[(5 + a)*(9 + a)]

$a^2 + 14\,a + 45$

The term "solve" can be used to solve equations for a particular variable.

⊟ solve 2x − 7 = 0 for x  ⋯

📑 step-by-step solution    🌟 full Wolfram|Alpha results

> Solve[−7 + 2*x == 0, x]

$$\left\{\left\{x \rightarrow \frac{7}{2}\right\}\right\}$$

The previous result contains a few conventions that will be explained in later chapters. The result should overall be pretty intuitive that the solution is $\frac{7}{2}$ when solving for *x*.

The results of the previous calculation can be referenced with the term "result," which in this case approximates the fraction $\frac{7}{2}$ to two digits.

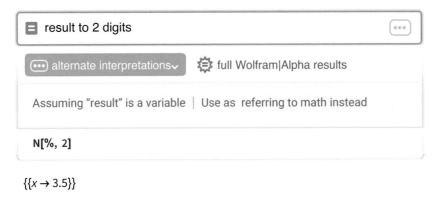

$\{\{x \rightarrow 3.5\}\}$

The term "solve" can be used with multiple equations and in solving for multiple variables.

> solve (2x − 7 = 0, 3x − 2y = 0) for x and y ···

📝 step-by-step solution    ⚙ full Wolfram|Alpha results

Solve[{−7 + 2∗x == 0, 3∗x − 2∗y == 0}, {x, y}]

$\left\{\left\{x \rightarrow \frac{7}{2}, y \rightarrow \frac{21}{4}\right\}\right\}$

Wolfram|Alpha Notebook Edition contains a powerful symbolic engine, so a calculation can solve an equation where the coefficients are symbols rather than numeric values.

> solve a ∗ x^2 + b ∗ x + c = 0, for x ···

⚙ full Wolfram|Alpha results

Solve[c + b∗x + a∗x^2 == 0, x, MaxExtraConditions −> Automatic]

$$\left\{\left\{x \rightarrow \frac{-\sqrt{b^2 - 4ac} - b}{2a}\right\}, \left\{x \rightarrow \frac{\sqrt{b^2 - 4ac} - b}{2a}\right\}\right\}$$

At this point, the reader's notebook containing these inputs likely has an "Untitled-1" tag at the top of the notebook. This indicates the notebook is not saved. To save a copy of the notebook, click the **File** drop-down menu and choose **Save As**. A new window will appear prompting for a file name and a location for the file. While Wolfram|Alpha Notebook Edition requires an internet connection to run, by default, notebook files are saved on the local machine.

The term "graph" can be used to create a 2D graphic where the domain goes from −10 to 10.

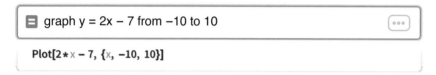

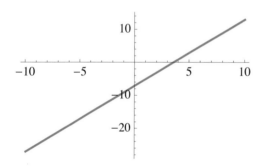

Many types of equations can be graphed, including trigonometric functions.

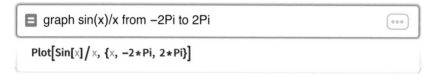

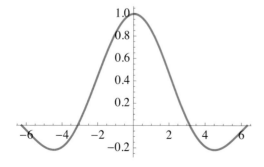

If two variables are used, Wolfram|Alpha Notebook Edition creates a surface plot automatically.

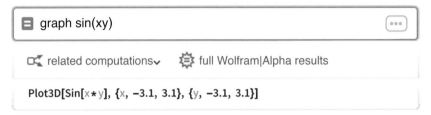

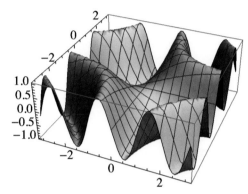

---

 For any 3D plot, you can left-click with the mouse and drag to rotate the plot for alternate views.

The term "table" can be used to create a table of values. In this case, the output is a list of values of $i^2$ where $i$ goes from 1 to 10.

$\{1, 4, 9, 16, 25, 36, 49, 64, 81, 100\}$

The term "result" can refer to either an equation or a list of numeric values. Graphing the result creates a list plot since the previous result was a list of numbers.

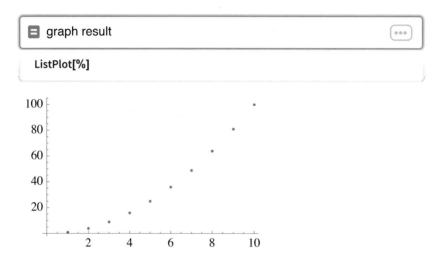

Many terms or phrases can be used to calculate an integral, including the term "integrate."

$-\cos(x) + c_1$

Note that the results include a constant $c_1$ of integration.

A matrix can be represented with nested parentheses, and can be used in linear algebra calculations.

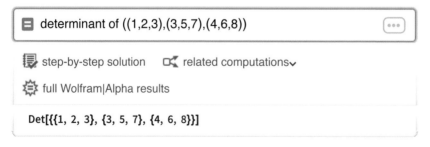

0

Saving this notebook was recommended earlier in the chapter, and resaving the notebook is recommended at this point in the chapter. Notebooks are not saved automatically, so clicking the **File** drop-down menu and choosing **Save** is necessary to save the final set of inputs and outputs from this chapter.

## Conclusion

This chapter outlines several common inputs to practice entering calculations into Wolfram|Alpha Notebook Edition. While the book will often recommend one particular term or phrase, phrasing in calculations is flexible and not limited to that one term or phrase. This provides a very efficient way to enter calculations and eliminates the need to memorize phrasing. In practice, different users of the software often form different habits in the phrasing of their respective calculations.

## Exercises

1. Calculate the number of seconds in a non-leap year by multiplying $60 * 60 * 24 * 365$.

2. Create variables $a$ and $b$, set them to 6 and 7, respectively, and find their product.

3. Create a plot of the function $5 \sin\left(\frac{1}{x}\right)$.

4. Replace the 5 in Exercise 3 with $\cos\left(\frac{1}{y}\right)$ to plot a new function.

5. Evaluate the values of the cubes of the first 10 odd numbers, then plot the result.

6. Define $g(x)$ as $\log(x + 1)$, and use it to calculate $g(0)$.

7. Calculate the values for $x$ such that $x^5 - 4x^4 - 5x^3 + 20x^2 + 4x - 16 = 0$.

8. Use **Solve** to find $a$ and $b$ such that $a * (1, 2, 3) + b * (4, 5, 6) = (7, 8, 9)$. Make sure that $a$ and $b$ are unset from Exercise 2.

9. Use **Differentiate** and **Integrate** to show that for any integrable function $f(x)$, the derivative of the integral of $f(x)$ is again $f(x)$ (which is the fundamental theorem of calculus). You can do this with any specific function.

10. Write the first 314 digits of $\pi$.

# Inputting Calculations into Wolfram|Alpha Notebook Edition

## Introduction

Wolfram|Alpha Notebook Edition is an interactive environment where calculations are often entered and then refined and reevaluated to explore or explain an idea. Through the growth of Wolfram|Alpha technology over time, Wolfram|Alpha Notebook Edition provides a very flexible way to enter calculations using everyday English, and does not require any rigid sequence to enter commands, nor any rigid syntax. Often, there are many terms or phrases that can be used to enter a calculation, meaning that each user can enter calculations in phrasing that is intuitive to them. In addition, Wolfram|Alpha Notebook Edition can recommend related commands to make exploring a concept even more efficient. This chapter will outline how the software performs calculations in more detail so the reader can more efficiently create their own calculations.

## Basic Navigation and Formatting

If Wolfram|Alpha Notebook Edition has just been launched, a new notebook can be created by clicking the **New Document** button on the welcome screen. A new notebook will appear with one blank input cell, which can be used for the first calculation in the notebook.

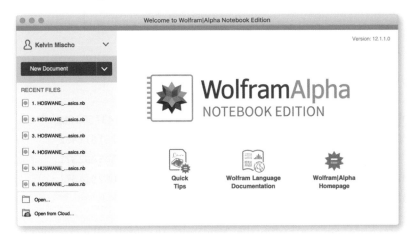

Keep in mind an internet connection is needed to log in to the software and to perform calculations.

The term "cell" is used to represent various content in a notebook, and each cell has a blue marker on the right of the screen. A notebook is just a collection of various cells, and a notebook can contain textual cells, cells containing calculations or cells containing results for calculations, including graphics. Many cells include content that spans only one line, but cells can wrap to multiple lines as needed. This is useful for lengthier calculations or text cells that include many sentences formatted as a paragraph.

 This book was written directly in notebooks, with one notebook for each chapter. So far in this chapter, there have been many types of cells for various titles, sections and text, each with its own blue cell marker to the right of the notebook. These cell markers show where that content begins and ends.

This chapter will focus on input cells used for calculations. A straightforward calculation of 2 to the 1,000th power can be used to demonstrate the basics, and aid in understanding the underlying technology when Wolfram|Alpha Notebook Edition performs calculations. A new notebook contains one input cell for a first calculation. After typing "2^1000" into this input cell, the Enter key can be pressed to perform the calculation and display the result.

10 715 086 071 862 673 209 484 250 490 600 018 105 614 048 117 055 336 074 437 503 883 ∴.
703 510 511 249 361 224 931 983 788 156 958 581 275 946 729 175 531 468 251 871 452 ∴.
856 923 140 435 984 577 574 698 574 803 934 567 774 824 230 985 421 074 605 062 371 ∴.
141 877 954 182 153 046 474 983 581 941 267 398 767 559 165 543 946 077 062 914 571 ∴.
196 477 686 542 167 660 429 831 652 624 386 837 205 668 069 376

Several new cells are created after evaluating the calculation. The input cell is extended to include any available suggestions for related calculations, an additional input cell is created that includes the Wolfram Language interpretation of the input and a separate output cell is created to display the result of the calculation.

The additional input cell containing the Wolfram Language uses a specific syntax and is the underlying language in all Wolfram technology. It is important to remember that users do not need to understand the Wolfram Language to use Wolfram|Alpha Notebook Edition, and many users of Wolfram|Alpha Notebook Edition will likely disregard that section of an input cell entirely. But it is useful to understand how Wolfram|Alpha Notebook Edition uses the Wolfram Language in the background to perform calculations.

The Wolfram Language section of the input cell is very useful specifically for high-school or junior-college students who will move on to use Mathematica at the university level. Mathematica will allow plain English input just like Wolfram|Alpha Notebook Edition, but many problems at the university level will require the additional resource of the Wolfram Language to extend and expand on what has been learned with Wolfram|Alpha Notebook Edition.

In practice, Wolfram|Alpha Notebook Edition sends the everyday English contained in an input cell for a calculation to Wolfram servers for interpretation. The server returns an expression in the form of Wolfram Language syntax, which is then evaluated on the user's local machine. So while it is not necessary for the user to understand the Wolfram Language to use Wolfram|Alpha Notebook Edition, this is the mechanism the software uses to perform calculations.

Most users will not focus on the Wolfram Language input cell when doing day-to-day calculations.

Why not have all the technology installed on a local machine? The main advantage is that technology on Wolfram servers is frequently updated and improved. So even if the local software installation is the same, input cells can be increasingly useful over time and accept more types of phrases as the technology on Wolfram servers expands to understand new phrases.

This first calculation uses the default styling, but a menu is available to set a notebook's behavior and minimize some of the extra cells that are included, if desired. This drop-down menu can be found by locating the gear icon at the top-right corner of a notebook. The **Hide Wolfram Language Inputs** option in this **Appearance** drop-down menu can be used to minimize all Wolfram Language input cells for the entire notebook.

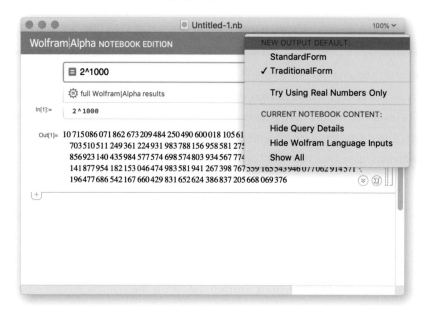

After hiding the Wolfram Language input cell, the notebook contains only the Wolfram|Alpha Input cell, the list of available suggestions and the output cell with the result of the calculation, and takes on a more streamlined style.

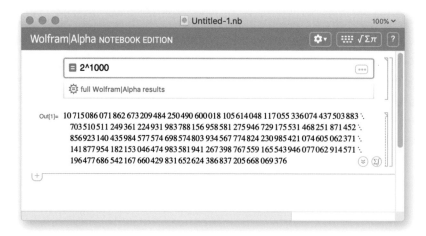

The same menu can also be used to hide the available suggestions by choosing the **Hide Query Details** option in the **Appearance** menu. In this case, hiding the related calculations minimizes the button for full Wolfram|Alpha results.

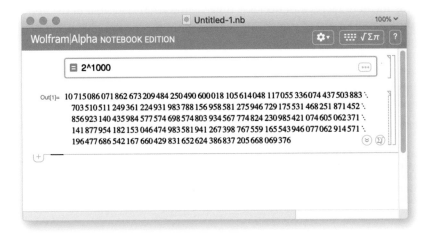

The buttons for related calculations and full Wolfram|Alpha results will be outlined in more detail later in this chapter. These buttons can be very useful and are often not minimized by the user when creating calculations.

To revert back to the default styling, the **Show All** option under the **Appearance** menu will add the Wolfram Language input cell and list of related calculations to all input cells in the notebook.

In addition to hiding portions of an input cell, the **Appearance** menu can restyle all results in output cells to **StandardForm**. **StandardForm** follows the conventions of the Wolfram Language, while **TraditionalForm** follows the styling conventions of a typical textbook.

In general, use of **StandardForm** is mostly valuable to users who intend to migrate to Mathematica or another software that uses the Wolfram Language. For everyday use of Wolfram|Alpha Notebook Edition, **TraditionalForm** will likely be the better choice.

Another common alteration to the default styling of a notebook is increasing the magnification. The default magnification for a notebook is 100%, and increasing this to 125% or 150% increases the size of all content in the notebook. Increasing the magnification is often useful when presenting content in a notebook with a projector in a classroom or with screensharing. This menu to increase or decrease the magnification is located in the upper-right corner of a notebook on macOS operating systems, or in the lower-right corner of a notebook on Windows operating systems.

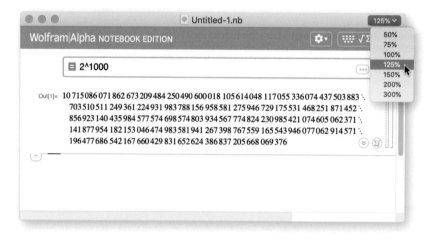

 When a notebook is saved, all the settings above are saved with the file, which is useful when opening the file on another day for a demonstration or to add content to the notebook.

## Methods for Entering Input Cells

When a new notebook is created, the first input cell is created automatically. There are several methods to create additional input cells.

A new cell is inserted at the position of the horizontal bar in the notebook. By default, the horizontal bar is placed just below the previous result, but this horizontal bar can be moved to any position in the notebook to insert new content above previous calculations or textual information.

The horizontal bar also acts as a shortcut to insert different types of cells. The plus icon can be clicked to display a list of cell types for this new cell. **Wolfram|Alpha Input** is the first choice in the list.

Remember Wolfram|Alpha Input cells are also the default type of cell. So when a user starts typing, a new Wolfram|Alpha Input cell is created at the position of the horizontal bar for this new calculation.

After filling in this second Wolfram|Alpha Input cell and pressing the Enter key, the results of the second calculation are displayed just below the first calculation in the notebook.

The **Format** drop-down menu is another method to insert new cells, and is a useful way to learn the keyboard shortcuts for inserting various types of cells. Similar to the insertion assistant in the horizontal bar, choosing a cell type in the **Format** menu will insert that cell at the position of the horizontal bar.

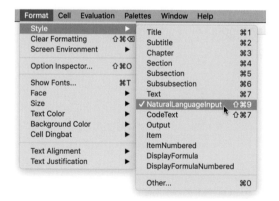

After using Wolfram|Alpha Notebook Edition to create a few notebooks, many users prefer using the keyboard shortcuts to insert new cells since it is often the fastest way to create new content, especially for textual content. For example, pressing the Command or Alt key with the 4 key will insert a new section cell at the position of the horizontal bar.

A later chapter will discuss textual cells in more detail and show more examples of building up content in a notebook with several different styles of text cells.

Calculations do not have to be created or evaluated in sequential order from the top of the notebook to the bottom of the notebook. Clicking above the first calculation will move the horizontal bar to the top of the notebook, and then any of the previous methods for creating a new Wolfram|Alpha Input cell can be used to insert a new calculation at the top of the notebook.

As calculations are created, a notebook always labels the calculations in order of evaluation. In the notebook in the above screenshot, the In[1] tag shows that 2^1000 was the first calculation of the session, the In[2] tag shows 2^10,000 was the second calculation of the session and 2^10,000 > 200^1000 was the third calculation of the session, even though it is located above the other calculations.

 The cell tags might not seem very important for arithmetic calculations, but when a notebook defines variables or functions, the order of calculations is more important. The software remembers a definition for any future calculation, even when that calculation is inserted above the definition in the notebook.

A calculation can be deleted from a notebook by highlighting the outer blue cell marker on the right side of the screen, then right-clicking with the mouse and choosing the **Cut** option.

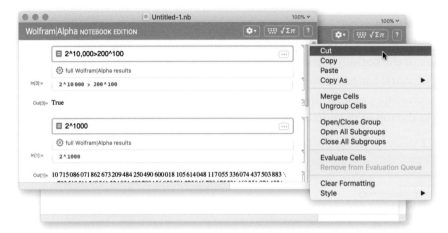

Calculations can be reordered with a similar operation. After highlighting the outer blue cell marker and right-clicking with the mouse, the option to cut (or copy) the cell can be chosen instead. After repositioning the horizontal bar to the desired location in the notebook, right-clicking again and choosing the **Paste** option will paste the cell in the new position in the notebook. The original calculation can then be deleted.

Instead of deleting entire calculations, a similar operation can be used to delete just the results of a calculation. After highlighting only the blue cell marker corresponding to the result and right-clicking with the mouse, the **Cut** option can be used to delete only the result while keeping the Wolfram|Alpha Input cell intact.

While deleting just the results might seem only occasionally useful, this is a very common operation when creating supplemental materials for a course. After creating the examples and testing the calculations, deleting the results allows the instructor to evaluate calculations in front of a group of students and pose questions before the students see the results.

For lengthier notebooks (or, for example, a teacher creating a quiz with an answer key as one notebook and the student version as another notebook), instead of highlighting output cells one by one to delete results, the Alt key (or the Option key on macOS operating systems) provides a more efficient way to delete all the results in a notebook. Holding down the Alt key while clicking any output cell in a notebook will highlight all cells of that type. After all the output cells containing results are highlighted, right-clicking with the mouse and choosing **Cut** will delete all the results in the entire notebook at once.

The **Edit** drop-down menu also includes options to **Cut**, **Copy** and **Paste**, which can be used instead of right-clicking with the mouse. The typical keyboard shortcuts for **Cut**, **Copy** and **Paste** also work for these operations to delete or move cells within a notebook.

This chapter is focused on Wolfram|Alpha Input cells for calculations, but all the methods for deleting or moving cells within a notebook work identically for any type of cell, including text cells, which will be outlined in more detail in a later chapter.

## Related Computations and Full Wolfram|Alpha Results

So far in this chapter, calculations have been manually typed one at a time to create a simple notebook. However, after evaluation, certain calculations display a **related computations** button and a **full Wolfram|Alpha results** button, both of which can be used to automatically create additional calculations or graphics related to the original calculation.

After creating a graph of an equation, the **related computations** button can be clicked to display a list of choices for other calculations that are potentially useful based on the original calculation.

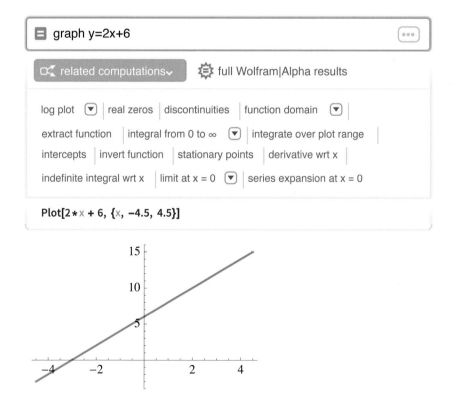

Clicking any of the choices creates a new calculation below the original one. After clicking the **real zeros** options, a new calculation to solve the equation where *y* equals 0 is created and automatically evaluated.

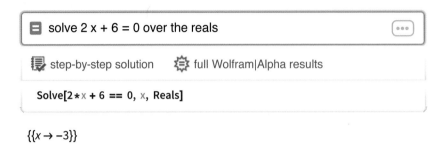

$$\{\{x \to -3\}\}$$

 The calculations created using related computations can also be a nice guide for useful phrases that can be included in calculations, like "over the reals" in the previous calculation.

Clicking the **log plot** option creates another new calculation to graph the equation on a log scale.

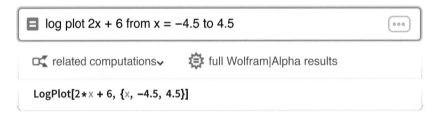

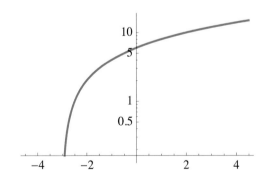

The new calculation is always inserted just below the original calculation so the user can easily inspect the results of the last calculation without having to scroll through the other related computations.

In addition to related computations, the **full Wolfram|Alpha results** button can be used to display related results styled after Wolfram|Alpha. Wolfram|Alpha always displays a collection of results organized in a series of pods. For this particular calculation, the **full Wolfram|Alpha results** displays the plot, along with a list of properties including the $x$ intercept, $y$ intercept and slope.

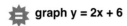 **graph y = 2x + 6**

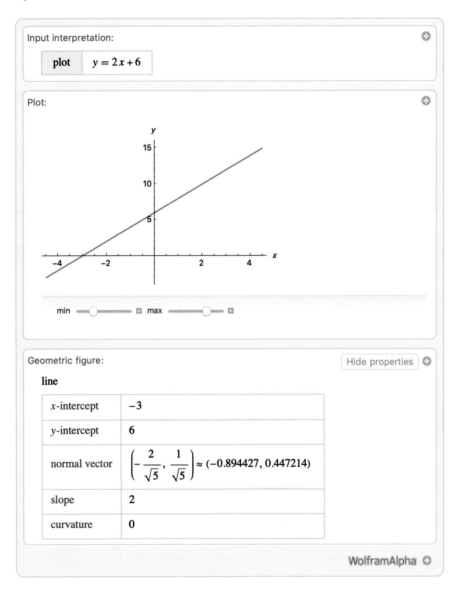

Input interpretation:

| plot | $y = 2x + 6$ |

Plot:

min ⟶○⟶ ⊞ max ⟶○⟶ ⊞

Geometric figure:　　　　　　　　　　　　　　　　　Hide properties

**line**

| $x$-intercept | $-3$ |
| $y$-intercept | $6$ |
| normal vector | $\left(-\dfrac{2}{\sqrt{5}}, \dfrac{1}{\sqrt{5}}\right) \approx (-0.894427, 0.447214)$ |
| slope | $2$ |
| curvature | $0$ |

WolframAlpha ○

The styling for calculations to generate full Wolfram|Alpha results is different than the default style of calculations in Wolfram|Alpha Notebook Edition. While full Wolfram|Alpha results can provide useful insights, none of the results can be referenced in later calculations. In the previous chapter, terms like "that" and "result" were used to reference a previous result, and that style of calculations only works for Wolfram|Alpha Notebook Edition input cells.

## Special Characters Keyboard

Many calculations can be stated in everyday English in Wolfram|Alpha Notebook Edition, but the software contains a keyboard menu with typeset characters that can be used in calculations to more closely mirror the style of a textbook. Symbols like $\pi$ and $\infty$ are available, as well as symbols to perform calculations like indefinite integration, summation or partial derivatives using notation that is commonly found in textbooks.

Wolfram|Alpha Pro has a very similar set of buttons, and the two can be used in a very similar style. The main difference is that Wolfram|Alpha Notebook Edition puts these symbols in calculations in a notebook so they can be saved and used in a series of calculations or visualizations.

The set of symbols appears after clicking the **Enter special characters** button at the upper-right-hand side of a notebook. The symbols are docked at the top of the notebook to make it easy to insert symbols in calculations in a lengthy notebook.

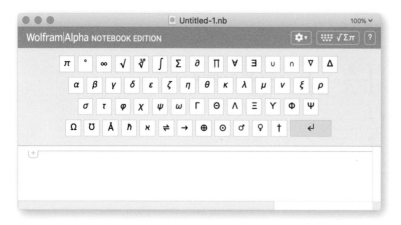

Clicking any of the buttons inserts the symbol at the position of the cursor in any calculation. The $\pi$ button can be used to approximate $\pi$ to 100 places.

3.14159265358979323846264338327950288419716939937510582097494459230781640$\dot{}$.
62862089986280348253421170 68

Symbols can be used to enter an indefinite integral, which includes a square root. For this particular calculation, related computations are also available, and these buttons to automatically create additional calculations work identically if the original calculation uses typeset symbols.

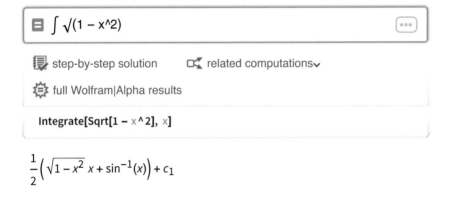

$$\frac{1}{2}\left(\sqrt{1-x^2}\,x + \sin^{-1}(x)\right) + c_1$$

## Step-by-Step Solutions

In addition to the related computations and full Wolfram|Alpha results, many types of calculations also display a **step-by-step solution** button. While the main result for calculations in Wolfram|Alpha Notebook Edition is only the final result of a calculation, the software contains a sophisticated set of solvers to display step-by-step solutions for many of the problems in precollege- or college-level mathematics.

The last calculation in the previous section of this chapter is one example that includes a step-by-step solution for solving the integral. Clicking the **step-by-step solution** button creates a new calculation in the notebook specific to the step-by-step solution. Or, like the following example, typing "show steps" as part of the calculation displays the step-by-step solution immediately in the result.

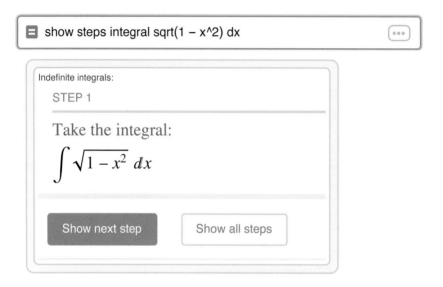

Wolfram|Alpha Pro also includes step-by-step solutions, and the earlier chapter on step-by-step solutions in Wolfram|Alpha Pro is relevant to Wolfram|Alpha Notebook Edition. Both display the same buttons for navigating through step-by-step solutions for a wide variety of problems. The difference is that step-by-step solutions for several problems can be saved in a notebook for later reference in Wolfram|Alpha Notebook Edition.

The result of this new calculation shows the major steps for solving this integral. The steps of the solution can be shown one at a time to act as a real-time quiz for the user, or the steps can be shown all at once to aid in double-checking a manually created solution.

These step-by-step results are a live calculation in the software, making it possible to solve problems and see step-by-step solutions for a very wide variety of problems. The step-by-step solution technology also automatically recognizes the best method for solving a problem, and the user does not need to know what particular course topic or course concept is best for solving a particular problem.

Typical uses for step-by-step solutions will be outlined in later chapters with common calculations in prealgebra, algebra, trigonometry, precalculus and calculus.

# Defining Variables and Functions

A previous chapter showed a simple example of creating a variable definition, and these types of calculations can be very useful when creating a series of calculations. It is sometimes useful to set a specific value for a variable related to algebraic calculations, or define a function when working on problems related to calculus.

The term "set" can be used to assign a value of 5 to the symbol $a$. This is one possible term, and "define" is another commonly used term to define variables.

5

When the symbol $a$ is included in any later calculations, the value of 5 is used in the calculation. In the following calculation, the result is 5 times 5 plus 6.

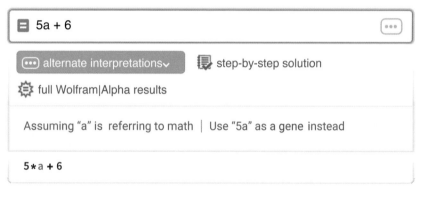

31

An earlier section in this chapter outlined the process for inserting new calculations above the current calculation. When variables are defined, they retain their values even for calculations performed in an earlier section of a notebook. The software stores this value based on the order of the calculations in the session, not the order of calculations in the notebook.

A new calculation can be inserted at any position in the notebook to unset the value of *a*.

**unset a**

a =.

After clearing the value of *a*, any previous calculations using *a* will retain their results based on the former value of *a*. If those calculations are reevaluated after clearing the value of *a*, the results will then show that *a* has no stored value. In this example, evaluating or reevaluating the calculation for 5 *a* + 6 will return an equation using *a* as a symbol.

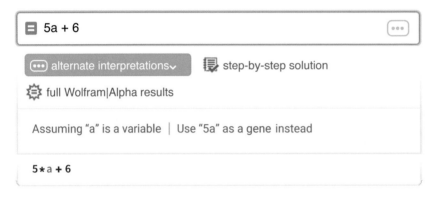

**5a + 6**

•••• alternate interpretations⌄   step-by-step solution

full Wolfram|Alpha results

Assuming "a" is a variable  |  Use "5a" as a gene instead

$5 * a + 6$

$5\,a + 6$

This convention of not updating previous results is useful if a particular symbol is used multiple times for different calculations in a notebook. The earlier examples retain their values and are independent of any new series of calculations using that same variable name.

Functions can also be defined using the term "set" along with conventions for functions outlined in a typical textbook.

**set f(x) = x^2 + 5**

full Wolfram|Alpha results

$f[x\_] := x^2 + 5$

Once a function $f$ is defined, it can be used in later calculations, including a calculation to create a graph of the function.

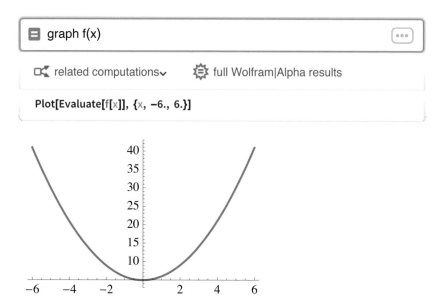

Similar to variables, the definition of $f$ will be applied for any calculation in the notebook that is evaluated after the function definition is established. The software stores this value based on the order of the calculations in the session, not the order of calculations in the notebook. At any position in the notebook, the term "clear" can be used to remove the definition of $f(x)$.

Any later calculation that uses $f$ will return a result showing that $f$ is no longer a defined function.

| f(5) | ... |
|------|-----|

$f(5)$

Later chapters on precalculus and calculus will outline function definitions in more detail, including how to use those function definitions to calculate derivatives or other common calculations in calculus.

## Storing Wolfram|Alpha Notebooks

Notebooks can be created in either a local installation of Wolfram|Alpha Notebook Edition or a web browser running Wolfram|Alpha Notebook Edition, and the process for storing a notebook is slightly different for a local installation compared to browser-based use of the software.

When using a local installation of Wolfram|Alpha Notebook Edition, any new notebook is given the name "Untitled-1," which is displayed at the top of the notebook. The **File** drop-down menu is used to save a notebook to a local machine by choosing the **Save As** option and giving the notebook a unique name. As content is added to a notebook, it is not resaved automatically, so clicking the **File** drop-down menu and choosing **Save** is recommended as new content is added. All content is captured in a saved notebook, and the document will look identical when opened in the future.

After a notebook is saved to a local machine with a particular file name, the **Save As** option in the **File** drop-down menu can be used again to save a second copy of the notebook. The second copy of the file could contain an answer key, or instructor notes, or less organized experimentation that is useful to retain but might not be appropriate to include in the final copy of the file that will be shared with students or colleagues.

When using Wolfram|Alpha Notebook Edition within a web browser, any new notebook is given a name "(unnamed)," which is displayed at the top left of the notebook. Clicking the "(unnamed)" text will display an input field to specify a unique name and store that notebook in the user's list of browser-based notebooks. All of a user's notebooks are listed under the **Cloud Files** menu.

When adding content to a notebook within a web browser, any new content is saved automatically, and it is not necessary to manually resave the notebook.

While the management of files is slightly different in a local installation versus browser-based use of Wolfram|Alpha Notebook Edition, notebook files stored on a local machine can easily be copied into the collection of cloud files for use in the browser-based version of the software. Notebooks stored in the browser-based version of the software can also be downloaded and opened with a local installation of the software.

The **Upload File (s)** button in the **Cloud Files** menu is used to copy a local notebook file into the collection of cloud files for the use of Wolfram|Alpha Notebook Edition in a web browser.

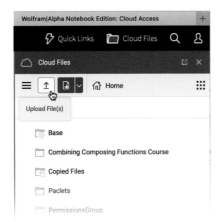

The **File** menu in the browser-based version of Wolfram|Alpha Notebook Edition can be used to download a notebook file and store it as a local file for use in a local installation of the software.

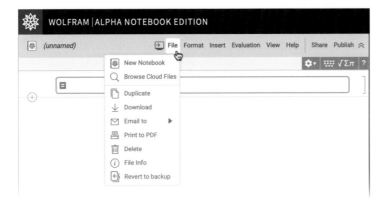

A later chapter will outline how to share files with a group of people, which could be collaborators, colleagues or students in a course.

## Conclusion

Notebooks are a flexible way to start and edit a series of calculations, and the structure of notebooks supports exploration of a concept through a series of calculations and visualizations that can be edited at any time. This is useful to prepare materials to outline an idea to colleagues or students, and it is useful to show live calculations that support real-time discussion of ideas. This can be done in simple, everyday activities that teachers and students always need: lesson plans, presentations, student lab reports, rubrics, assessment outcome reports, interactive models and much more.

## Exercises

1. Calculate the following: $3\,\hat{}\,5$.

2. Calculate the average of the following list of numbers: 3, 5, 6, 10.

3. Solve the following equation for $a$: $3\,a + 6 = 0$.

4. Create a new calculation to display the step-by-step solution for the answer to Exercise 3.

5. Find the melting point of iron.

6. Convert the above temperature to Fahrenheit.

7. Integrate $3\,x\,\hat{}\,3 + 5\,x\,\hat{}\,2 - 6\,x + 3$.

8. Take the previous output and find the solution in which 1 is substituted for $x$.

9. Use the **Special Characters** keyboard to find the integral of $3\,x\,\hat{}\,2 + \text{pi}$.

10. Find the area of a circle that is three centimeters in diameter.

# Word Processing and Typesetting in Wolfram|Alpha Notebook Edition

## Introduction

In addition to calculations, notebooks can include supporting text to explain results. Wolfram|Alpha Notebook Edition includes many types of textual cells with predefined formatting, along with many options for restyling text. This makes Wolfram|Alpha Notebook Edition a useful environment for course notes, supplemental materials for a course, lectures or presentations, or as a scratchpad for exploring ideas.

## The Structure of Notebooks

A notebook in Wolfram|Alpha Notebook Edition is just a collection of various types of cells, and those cells can be either input cells for calculations or cells with textual content. While individual text cells can be restyled in terms of size, font or coloring, notebooks include a predefined list of text cells, each with different formatting. Title cells are text cells with a larger font to act as a title for a document. Text cells are cells with a smaller font for paragraphs of text. Other types of text cells include subtitle, chapter, section, subsection, subsubsection and ItemNumbered.

---

Restyling specific text within a cell will be outlined later in this chapter. That process is normally useful for specific words or phrases.

The Cell Insertion Assistant can be used to create any type of cell, including text cells. A title cell can be inserted in a notebook by clicking the plus icon located at the left of the horizontal bar and choosing **Title**. A title cell will be inserted at the position of the horizontal bar, and the cursor will be positioned in that cell to accept content.

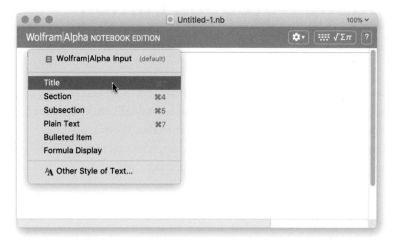

Additional cells can be created by clicking the mouse in the desired position to move the horizontal bar, then the same Cell Insertion Assistant can be used again to create a new cell in the position of the horizontal bar. A section cell has a slightly smaller font than a title cell, and is typically used as a marker for major topics in a notebook.

For readers creating documents with several types of cells for the first time, it is sometimes easier to watch a video to see the process of creating various types of cells. This video (wolfr.am/hostwane) starts with a blank notebook and shows the process of creating new calculations as well as new text cells.

After typing in content for the section cell, the process can be repeated to create a plain text cell below the section cell. By default, the various types of cells are formatted with their own coloring and styling.

 The choice of **Other Styles of Text...** in the Cell Insertion Assistant can be used to see a larger list of available cell types for a notebook.

Text cells also have accompanying blue cell markers to the right of the screen, just like input cells. These blue cell markers have a hierarchy, with the title cell at the top. A notebook also contains additional blue cell markers to represent larger groups of cells.

The blue cell markers can be used to minimize content in a notebook. Double-clicking the outermost cell for the group of cells in the notebook will minimize the section and text cells, and only the title cell will be displayed. A new arrow is created next to the text in the title cell to signal there is minimized content, and the outermost cell also changes to display an arrow at the bottom of the outer cell, also signaling there is minimized content. Clicking the arrow icon next to the text in the title cell or double-clicking the outermost blue cell marker will display the section and text cells, and the notebook will revert to its original form.

There are a variety of reasons to minimize content. This approach is useful when given a presentation to prevent the audience from reading ahead. It is also sometimes useful when creating a notebook to minimize a finished section to fully concentrate on new content.

This grouping of cells exists for the section and text cells as well. After all the cells are displayed, double-clicking the outer cell that bounds only the section and text cells will minimize just the text cells. The section cell now contains an arrow icon that signals there is minimized content. The outer blue cell that bounds only the section and text cells also contains an arrow at the bottom, also signaling there is minimized content. Any cell that is part of a subgroup will be minimized, even for longer notebooks that contain multiple text cells or input cells within a subgroup of cells.

 In terms of hierarchy, a plain text cell and an input cell for calculations are equal. This means if a section contains both text and calculations, both will be minimized when minimizing all content in a section subgroup.

## Textual Cell Types

In addition to title cells, section cells and text cells, notebooks contain several other choices to structure the content. Any type of cell can be created with the Cell Insertion Assistant, but the **Format** drop-down menu is a useful alternative to create new text cells. This menu displays keyboard shortcuts for the most common types of text cells.

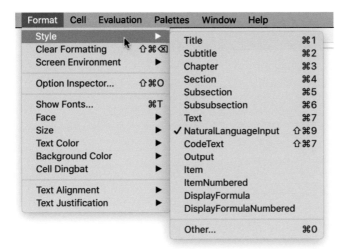

As an alternative to clicking the Cell Insertion Assistant or the **Format** menu, a new cell can be created by positioning the horizontal bar in the desired location and then pressing the corresponding keyboard shortcut to create that type of cell. After users are familiar with notebooks, these keyboard shortcuts are often the preferred method of creating new cells.

 The software will show Windows keyboard shortcuts if you are running Wolfram|Alpha Notebook Edition on Windows, and it will show macOS keyboard shortcuts if you are running the software on a macOS operating system.

The cell type ItemNumbered has a unique property where it automatically creates a sequential numbering for each cell of that type in a notebook. The numbering starts over when using this type of cell within a different subgroup of cells. If three ItemNumbered cells are created, they will automatically be numbered **1.**, **2.** and **3.**. Additional ItemNumbered cells contained under a different cell subgroup will be numbered starting with **1.** and not **4.**. This is useful for creating several sets of exercise questions for students, or several sets of bullet points for several topics in one notebook.

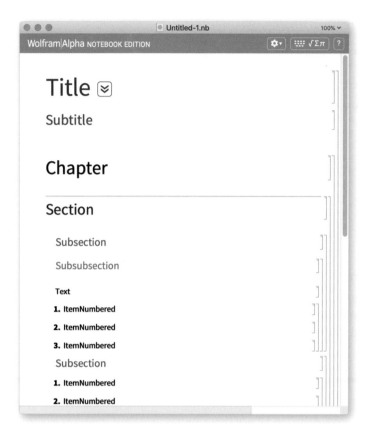

When giving a presentation, it is also possible to minimize multiple subgroups. The subsubsection subgroup could be minimized first to hide the plain text and ItemNumbered cells, then the section cell could be minimized to hide the subsection and subsubsection cells. When presenting, this allows the speaker to reveal the content progressively, even within the same section subgroup.

## Additional Styling for Cell Content

In addition to the default styling for various types of textual cells, any text cell can be restyled. This styling can either be applied to an entire cell or to certain words or phrases in one cell.

The available options are listed in the **Format** drop-down menu, and include changing the font, face, size, color or background color for any cell. After highlighting a word or phrase with the mouse, a user can restyle that content by choosing the corresponding option in the **Format** menu. In addition to highlighting single words or phrases within a cell, a user can highlight the blue cell marker, and the options within the **Format** menu will be applied to all text contained within that cell.

The following example includes several cases of restyling text, including text increased to a 24-point size, text recolored blue and text with a light-gray background.

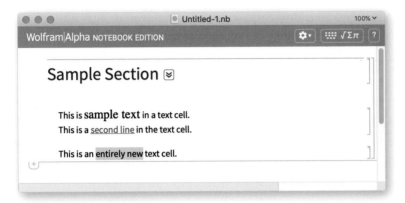

 Typical keyboard shortcuts can also be used to restyle text to be bold or italicized. The **Text Color** and **Background Color** menu options also contain choices for a palette to recolor text with finer control over the color and grayscale.

In addition to the **Format** drop-down menu, the **Writing Assistant** palette located in the **Format** drop-down menu in the desktop version of Wolfram|Alpha Notebook Edition also contains useful styling for text cells. This collection of buttons contains several of the same choices as the **Format** menu, but the button to restyle text as math cells or to draw a frame around a cell are two useful choices that only appear in this palette.

Frames can be added to any type of cell by highlighting a cell, then clicking **Frame** under the **Cell Properties** section in the palette and choosing the desired styling for the frame. This formatting can be useful for adding emphasis to certain content or highlighting a portion of a notebook and recommending the addition of new content.

Answer:

The **Math Cells** drop-down menu can be used to format formulas and improve clarity. The following two text cells include a formula with default styling, then the same formula formatted as an inline math cell, which is the first choice in the **Math Cells** drop-down menu.

$f(x)=3x^2+5$

$f'(x) = 3\,x^2 + 5$

Notebooks also contain a spellchecker, and by default, words that do not appear in the built-in dictionary will be underlined in red. Mousing over the underlined word will create a list of suggestions to replace the word with a word in the dictionary. For longer notebooks, the spelling can be checked for the entire notebook at once by clicking the **Edit** drop-down menu and choosing **Check Spelling**. A separate window will appear to guide the user through the process of replacing or skipping a word to keep the original word intact in the notebook.

Clicking the **Add Word** button will add a word to the dictionary, and the spellchecker will not flag this word in other notebooks.

## Showing Page Breaks for Printing

When a notebook contains lengthy text cells, the notebook will wrap words at the edge of the window. When clicking and dragging the corner of a notebook to resize the window, the word wrap will be updated automatically.

When a notebook is printed, however, the width of a printed page and the width of the notebook might not be the same. Clicking the **File** drop-down menu, choosing **Print Settings** and then choosing **Show Page Breaks** will display a print preview. New horizontal bars will appear to represent page breaks and a page count will be added to the bottom right of the notebook.

Clicking the **Print Settings** option in the **File** drop-down menu and deselecting **Show Page Breaks** will change the formatting back to the default view.

A later chapter will discuss sharing notebooks and saving notebooks in various formats, including PDF. A print preview can be useful for printing directly from the software to a printer, or for the process of creating a PDF file.

## Conclusion

Notebooks are a flexible way to create a series of calculations to explore a concept. Including text cells along with calculations is a useful way to outline a concept in more detail for the reader of a notebook. Text cells can also facilitate collaboration or discussion between an instructor and a student to fully discuss a concept, or between collaborators to fully outline a concept.

## Exercises

1. Create a new notebook with a title cell of "My First Notebook."

2. Add a subtitle with your name and the date.

3. Add a chapter called "My First Calculations."

# CHAPTER 8

4. Add a section called "Basic Math."

5. Add an input of "solve 3x + 5 = 11."

6. Change the date in your subtitle to be a blue color.

7. Add a second section called "Graphics."

8. Add a text cell under graphics that says "Here's an example of a sine curve."

9. Add an input of "graph sin(x)."

10. Add bold and italics to the phrase "sine curve" in your previous text cell.

# Presenting with Slide Shows in Wolfram|Alpha Notebook Edition

## Introduction

Previous chapters outlined the process of creating notebooks in Wolfram|Alpha Notebook Edition, which include a mixture of text, calculations, graphics and animations. The software also includes an alternate styling for notebooks called a presenter notebook. This styling has all the capabilities of a regular notebook, but adds buttons and menus to aid in creating and giving presentations where the notebook acts as a slide show.

## Creating a New Presenter Notebook

A new presenter notebook can be created by clicking the **File** drop-down menu, choosing **New** and then choosing **Presenter Notebook**. Alternatively, the welcome screen for Wolfram|Alpha Notebook Edition also contains an option to create a new presenter notebook by clicking the caret to the right of the red **New Document** button and choosing **Presenter Notebook**.

A new presenter notebook includes buttons and menus to guide a user through the process of creating a new slide show. The lower portion of the document is just a blank notebook.

## Adding Content to the Presentation

The same methods for creating cells can be used to create the content in the presenter notebook, including using the **Format** drop-down menu or keyboard shortcuts to insert various types of cells. To provide a clean-looking presentation, the Cell Insertion Assistant is not displayed in a presenter notebook, and the horizontal line that specifies the location for new cells is a plain horizontal line. Instead, a drop-down menu is provided at the top of the notebook to insert cells and the default choice is a section cell.

There is no difference between a presenter notebook and a regular notebook, other than the top bar. All of the options to minimize content, or restyle text cells, or create calculations work the same in a presenter notebook.

In some cases, a user might know beforehand that a slide show will be the desired format for a project, and a presenter notebook can act as the initial authoring environment for the content. In other cases, a user might create a plain notebook first that contains many calculations, with the intention of taking a subset of the content to create a slide show. For this second case, it is always possible to copy and paste cells from a plain notebook to a presenter notebook. The process is identical to moving cells within the same notebook. To copy a group of cells, the outer blue cell marker representing the desired group of cells can be highlighted, then copied using the **Edit** drop-down menu, then pasted into the presenter notebook in the desired location using the **Edit** drop-down menu. Just like any addition of new cells, the horizontal bar dictates where the subgroup of cells will be pasted in the presenter notebook.

As mentioned in previous chapters, it is common to keep multiple notebook files for a particular course lesson or project. At times, it might be convenient to have multiple copies that are each a plain notebook, but it is also common to have multiple copies where the content with an answer key is a plain notebook, and the content without the results or answers is saved as a presenter notebook.

## Styling the Presentation

Once the notebook is populated with content, the buttons and menus in the presenter notebook can be used to create a slide show. The first step is adding slide breaks to separate the content into multiple slides. For a lengthy notebook, clicking the **Slide Break Defaults** button creates a menu and allows a user to automatically create slide breaks above all cells of a certain type. In practice, a new slide often begins with a section cell or chapter cell, and this menu provides an easy way to create slide breaks prior to each section or chapter cell based on the style of the content.

When adding content or making finer edits, the **Insert New Slide** button can also be used to create a new slide break. The slide break will be inserted at the location of the horizontal bar.

In addition to adding slides, the **Presenter Tools** menu also provides choices to change fonts; make text bold, italicized or underlined; or change the color of text. Cells can also be highlighted with the blue cell marker and nudged in different directions using buttons to create indentation or different horizontal spacing as desired.

## Presentation Mode

Once the notebook has the desired content, styling and slide breaks, a user can begin a presentation by clicking the **Start Presentation** button at top right of the notebook. This toggles the presenter notebook to cover the full screen, eliminates the buttons and menus to control styling and resizes the content to fit the screen, often making all the text larger.

To navigate within a presentation, a drop-down menu is available at the upper-right corner of the presenter notebook.

The first set of choices allows a user to advance to the next slide, go back to the previous slide, display the first slide or display the last slide. Keyboard shortcuts for these choices are also available under the **Presentation Controls** menu option. By default, the Home key displays the first slide, the End key displays the last slide, the right arrow key advances to the next slide and the left arrow key goes back to the previous slide. All keyboard shortcuts can be changed by the user.

It is also common for users to display the navigation bar, which is the first choice in the second group of menu options. The navigation bar includes buttons to advance slides with the same set of options as the available keyboard shortcuts, as well as a drop-down menu to advance to a particular slide. The choices in the drop-down menu include the content at the top of the actual slides to aid in choosing the desired slide. In most cases, this menu includes the section or chapter cell at the top of the slide.

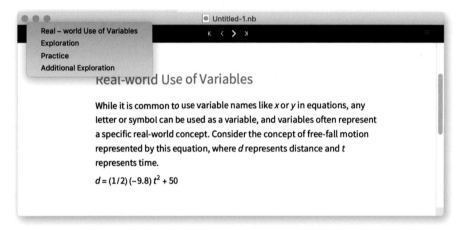

 Clicking the option **Toggle Full Screen** will end full-screen mode for a presentation, and the presenter notebook can be manually resized. This can be useful if the presentation also involves displaying webpages or other applications on that machine. The navigation bar and other styling will remain intact within this smaller window.

## Content Editing

Content can be edited or changed at any time within a presenter notebook, even in presentation mode. When presenting to a live audience, sliders for animations can be moved to show real-time effects on a graph when changing that parameter, or calculations can be altered and reevaluated to show different variations and examples very quickly.

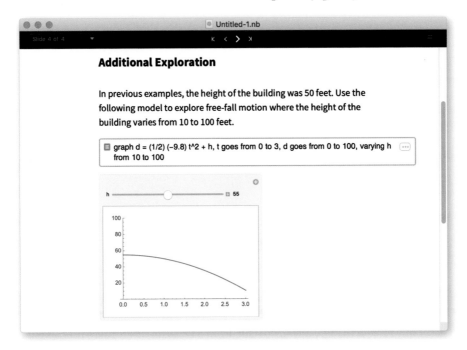

At the end of a presentation, a presenter notebook can be toggled back to the default styling by clicking the drop-down menu at the upper-right corner of the notebook and choosing the **End Presentation** option. The set of buttons to edit the slide show will be displayed and the presenter notebook will return to its original size. A presenter notebook can be saved just like any other notebook by clicking the **File** drop-down menu and choosing the **Save** or **Save As** options.

## Hyperlinks and Pictures in Presentations

In addition to the restyling of text cells outlined in a previous chapter, it is also possible to include hyperlinks within text cells in a notebook or insert pictures in the form of image files in a notebook. Both are useful to customize a presentation and provide the desired appearance.

A hyperlink can be created by first highlighting the desired word or phrase, then choosing the **Hyperlink** option in the **Insert** drop-down menu, and then entering the desired website URL in the "Other notebook or URL" input field.

It is usually easiest to copy a website URL from a browser, then paste that URL into the input field to insert a hyperlink. Once the URL is entered, the text containing the hyperlink will be restyled. Additional styling, like underlining the text, is possible after adding a hyperlink.

The **Insert** drop-down menu can also be used to include a picture in a notebook. A picture might be the only content in a cell, but it is also possible to include text along with the picture in the same cell. An image file can be inserted into a notebook by first clicking to position the cursor in the desired location within a cell, then choosing the **Picture from File** option in the **Insert** drop-down menu, then selecting the desired file from the directory of files on the local machine. After choosing the file, the image will be pasted into the notebook and can be resized by highlighting the image and dragging the corners with the mouse.

# Conclusion

While students often prefer regular notebooks when taking notes or creating their own projects or explorations, instructors often find presenter notebooks useful for lectures or discussions with students. The formatting of presenter notebooks is useful when a computer is connected to a projector to display content to a large audience, or when content is being shared through screensharing with students. Presenter notebooks give instructors the ability to answer questions in real time with live calculations, and a notebook acts as an immediate archive for those discussions for students to review as needed.

# Exercises

1. Open a new presenter notebook. Add a title cell and name it "My First Presentation."

2. Add your name as a presentation subtitle.

3. Add a new slide and copy a cell from an existing notebook.

4. Create a section cell called "New Section Cell" above the content that you just pasted. Use the cell action button in the Presenter Tools to align the section cell you just created in the center.

5. Add an image between the section cell and the content you originally pasted. Align the image with the section cell above.

6. Click at the end of the current slide and add a new slide by going to the Presenter Tools and choosing **Chapter** (plus slide break). Name the Chapter "Quadratic Equation".

7. Select the chapter you just entered and turn it into a hyperlink to the Wikipedia page on the quadratic equation.

8. Start the presentation. Edit the last slide while in presentation mode by solving for $x$ in the equation $a x^{\wedge}2 + b x + c = 0$.

9. Add an additional calculation for "graph 3x^2+6x+3."

10. End full screen (presentation mode) and save your presentation.

# Sharing Projects Created in Wolfram|Alpha Notebook Edition

## Introduction

Wolfram|Alpha Notebook Edition can be installed on a local computer as a local software application, or it can be run within a web browser with no required installation on that machine or device. This chapter will outline how content is stored in both cases, and will outline several approaches to share work with colleagues, students or any broad audience.

## Notebook Files

When running Wolfram|Alpha Notebook Edition on a local machine (a Windows or macOS computer), files are stored on that local machine with a file format of .nb. This stands for the term "notebook," which is the common way to refer to files in Wolfram|Alpha Notebook Edition.

 Many schools and colleges will have both Wolfram|Alpha Notebook Edition and Mathematica. They both have the same file format (.nb). An author of a notebook in Wolfram|Alpha Notebook Edition will be able to send the notebook to someone using Mathematica, and they will be able to work with the notebook seamlessly. The same is true in the other direction as well, so the author of a notebook does not need to be concerned about which product their intended audience is using.

Saved notebooks include all content created by the user, including text, calculations and the results for those calculations. The results are stored in the notebook, even if those results depend on other calculations to define variables or functions.

A local notebook file can be shared just like any other local file. Attaching a notebook file to an email is a common method to send a project to colleagues or students, or a notebook can be posted to a website or course materials page where colleagues or students can download that file to their respective machines. Wolfram|Alpha Notebook Edition also allows a notebook to be attached to an email. A user simply has to click the **File** drop-down menu and choose the **Send To** option, which displays a menu for drafting the email.

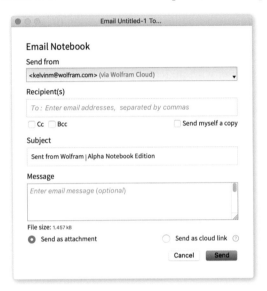

The email is created by specifying recipients, adding a subject for the email and writing text for the body of the message. The recipient of the email can save a new copy of the notebook to their machine after viewing or editing the file in their copy of Wolfram|Alpha Notebook Edition.

In some cases, an instructor will send a group of students the same notebook, which students can read and review to prepare for a quiz or test; in that case, students can add their own notes to their own local copy of the file.

## Notebooks in Printed or PDF Format

In cases where a recipient simply needs to read a notebook and will not edit or create calculations, saving a notebook as a PDF file can sometimes be useful for sharing the content.

A PDF copy of a notebook file can be created by clicking the **Save As** option in the **File** drop-down menu and specifying a file name. The file name for the .pdf file can be identical to the .nb file name, or the PDF can be renamed. This PDF file can be posted to a website or course materials page, or the file can be included as an attachment in an email.

In addition to creating a PDF file, a notebook's content can be shared by printing the file in paper form by clicking the **Print** option under the **File** drop-down menu. A previous chapter outlined the process to show page breaks in a notebook, and the process for creating a PDF file can give the user insight into how a notebook will appear when printed to paper as well.

In general, the styling and content in a notebook will be identical in a corresponding PDF version of the same file, or when the notebook is printed in paper form.

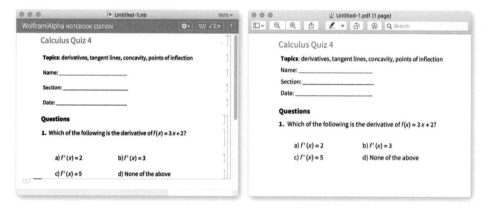

## Sharing and Publishing Web-Based Notebooks

In addition to installing Wolfram|Alpha Notebook Edition on a Windows or macOS machine, any user can also run Wolfram|Alpha Notebook Edition through a web browser. This web-based version does not require any installation, nor any plugin. Notebooks are viewed within a web browser and stored on Wolfram servers.

 A user can work with notebooks using a local installation of the software or web-based access to the software, or use both at different times. When using a macOS machine, a local installation might be preferred; when using a Chromebook, web-based access might be preferred.

The web-based version of Wolfram|Alpha Notebook Edition contains several useful menus for sharing notebooks that keep the notebooks in a convenient web-based format. The recipient can access the shared notebook on a wide variety of computers or devices by logging in to Wolfram|Alpha Notebook Edition through a web browser.

### SHARE Menu

An author can share a web-based notebook with a small group of recipients by clicking the **Share** menu and specifying the recipients using a list of email addresses.

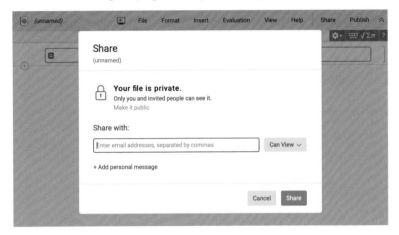

Recipients can be given editing privileges by clicking the drop-down menu to the right of the recipient list and choosing **Can Edit** instead of **Can View**. **View-only mode** is selected as the default option. The author can also add a personal message by clicking the **Add personal message** button, which displays an input field for that message.

 The email address in the list must also correspond to the recipient's login to Wolfram|Alpha Notebook Edition, which is called a Wolfram ID.

After clicking the **Share** button, each recipient receives a notification with a link to the web-based notebook. The recipient is prompted to log in to Wolfram|Alpha Notebook Edition when they click the hyperlink to the web-based notebook.

When a web-based notebook is shared using the **Share** menu, each recipient edits the same copy of the notebook as the author. If a recipient adds content to the notebook, that content will be displayed when the original author next accesses the web-based notebook. This menu for sharing a web-based notebook works well when each collaborator creates a different section of the same project.

## PUBLISH Menu

A web-based notebook can be shared with a larger group of recipients by clicking the **Publish** menu and creating a more generic website URL. This can be a more efficient process compared to typing a large list of email addresses into the **Share** menu.

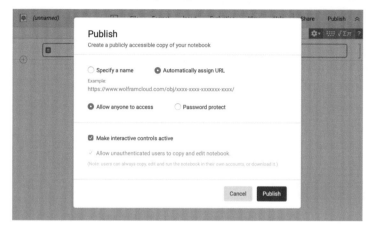

The first select box allows the author to specify a name for the published notebook or to accept an automatically assigned URL. The author can also password protect a published notebook by clicking the **Password protect** select box.

 In many cases, requiring a password for a published notebook is not necessary if the goal is to broadly share the content. However, in a course setting, it might be useful to provide a published notebook, then provide the password at a specific time when students will start to work on that project.

A confirmation is displayed after clicking the **Publish** button. The author is given the website URL for the published notebook, which can be immediately viewed or copied.

The web-based notebook can be shared with students or colleagues by including the URL in an email or, more commonly, by posting the URL on a webpage. When recipients click the URL, a preview of the web-based notebook is displayed in their browser. This approach accommodates many types of devices since clicking the URL on a tablet opens the published notebook in a browser on that tablet, or clicking the URL on a computer opens the published notebook in a browser on that computer.

The published notebook can be edited by either clicking the **Make Your Own Copy** button or clicking the **Download** button. The **Make Your Own Copy** button will prompt the recipient to log in to Wolfram|Alpha Notebook Edition to access the content as a web-based notebook. The **Download** button will create a local notebook file to access the content in a local installation of Wolfram|Alpha Notebook Edition.

 When considering whether to work within a browser to edit a notebook or work in a local installation to edit a notebook, neither choice has a major advantage over the other, which provides a lot of flexibility. A user or recipient of a web-based notebook might choose based on available hardware, or whether they plan to share content themselves, which will be outlined later in this chapter.

After a recipient logs in to Wolfram|Alpha Notebook Edition within a browser to edit the web-based notebook, the notebook will automatically be copied to the recipient's collection of web-based notebooks. To give the web-based notebook a different name, the recipient can click the existing file name in the top-left corner of the notebook and will then be prompted to type the new name.

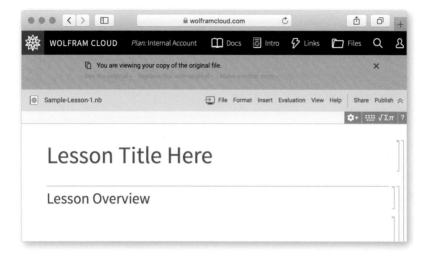

At this point, the recipient's web-based notebook is independent of the author's original published notebook. When the recipient edits content, that new content will not appear in the author's original published notebook.

 For courses, a published notebook is an effective way for an instructor to create an assignment and prompt all students to make their own copies of that web-based notebook. Then each student can make their own edits independent of one another.

The new notebook created by the recipient can be shared with the original author or with other students or colleagues by clicking either the **Share** menu or the **Publish** menu. The process to share a notebook for the first time is identical to the process to share an updated notebook, so the recipient would follow the steps outlined in this chapter to share an updated notebook with others.

 While the examples above outline the process of publishing a notebook while running the software within a browser, the **Publish** menu is also available in a local installation of Wolfram|Alpha Notebook Edition within the **File** drop-down menu. The menus and process of publishing a notebook are identical in a local installation of the software compared to the browser-based version of the software.

## Conclusion

Since notebooks are a useful environment for communicating ideas, sharing those ideas with a diverse audience is often an important component of a project. Wolfram|Alpha Notebook Edition provides many different options to share notebooks based on the audience, available hardware and specific situation.

## Exercises

1. If a team leader wanted to allow their team to add notes and comments to their notebook, would they use the **Publish** menu or the **Share** menu?

2. An instructor wants their students (>50) to have a copy of their notebook. What would be the most efficient menu to use in this case, **Publish** or **Share**?

3. If you want to receive an independent copy of your notebook with notes from a colleague, which menu would you choose, **Publish** or **Share**?

4. Four engineering students are working together on a group project and they need to turn in a single notebook with their work. What would be the most efficient method of setting up a collaborative notebook, publishing or sharing?

5. You are preparing for a workshop in which you are demonstrating multiple calculations in a notebook, and attendees will need to access the notebook. Would you want to publish or share your notebook?

6. What would be the most efficient method for sharing an independent notebook with a tech-savvy colleague who only uses the free Wolfram Player: emailing, sending a PDF, publishing or sharing?

7. You need to send a static notebook to your boss for illustration as part of their PDF presentation to university administration. What is the best way to send that document?

8. A colleague needs to send out a copy of their notebook before their group presentation. They ask you whether they should publish or share their notebook to your team of 15 people. How do you advise them?

9. When you email your notebook to someone through your notebook interface, does their email need to be associated with their Wolfram ID?

10. You are giving a talk at a virtual conference and you want to allow your audience to interact with some of the data that you are presenting. Would you publish or share your notebook?

# Prealgebra in Wolfram|Alpha Notebook Edition

## Introduction

Wolfram|Alpha Notebook Edition supports many types of calculations and visualizations that are useful for exploring concepts in prealgebra. The software contains a powerful engine for symbolic calculations that can be used to explore algebraic relationships and generate many types of graphs. This chapter includes a sampling of examples that can be used as a guide for how to use Wolfram|Alpha Notebook Edition in prealgebra, but is not an exhaustive list of available calculations.

## Working with Numbers

Calculations in Wolfram|Alpha Notebook Edition can take the form of fractions or decimals. If a calculation uses fractions, the result will also be a fraction.

Adding one-half and one-fourth will return a fraction of three-fourths.

The **related computations** menu was outlined in a previous chapter related to equations and creating various graphs, but that menu is available for many types of calculations. In this case, the suggestions are completely different and are related to fractions.

Subtracting fractions or multiplying fractions will also return a result in fraction form.

When performing multiple calculations with fractions, it is often useful to surround a fraction with parentheses. For example, the fraction one-fourth to the zero power can be entered with parentheses to specify the entire fraction is raised to the power of zero.

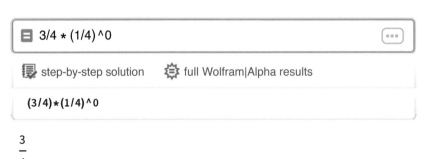

The phrase "as a decimal" can be used to provide a decimal approximation of any fraction. Calculations in Wolfram|Alpha Notebook Edition automate as many things as possible, and in this case, the software chooses two decimal places automatically. The user does not need to remember to specify that detail.

0.75

Converting a decimal to a fraction is also possible using similar phrasing.

$$\frac{3}{4}$$

For non-terminating fractions, the result is rounded to six decimal places. This quantity of decimal places is chosen by the software automatically to provide insight into the decimal form, while also using a reasonable amount of screen space.

0.666667

The **full Wolfram|Alpha results** button creates a new set of input and output cells to display the same pods as the Wolfram|Alpha website. These pods, which are boxes bounded by a gray border, provide both the result of the original calculation and related calculations or visualizations that are often also of interest. In this case, the second pod provides a button to extend the quantity of digits in the decimal approximation by clicking the **More digits** button.

 **2/3 as a decimal**

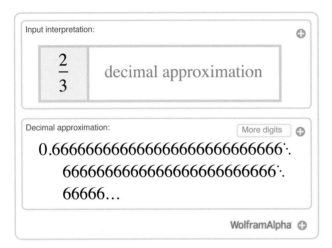

 While this calculation can also be entered into Wolfram|Alpha, Wolfram|Alpha Notebook Edition is a nice way to have several calculations together in one document for comparison.

The automation in previous calculations is useful, but it is also possible to include an explicit quantity of decimal places in a calculation to specify the format of the result in more detail.

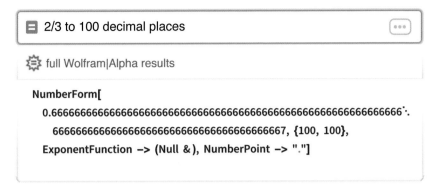

0.6666666666666666666666666666666666666666666666666666666666666666666666666666666666666666666666666666⁻.
666666666666666666666666666666667

In addition to converting a fraction to a decimal, very similar phrasing can be used to convert a fraction to a percentage.

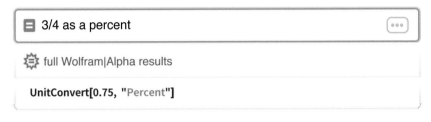

75.%

Wolfram|Alpha Notebook Edition contains a wide variety of built-in knowledge, including an understanding of percentages and the ability to perform calculations with percentages using everyday English.

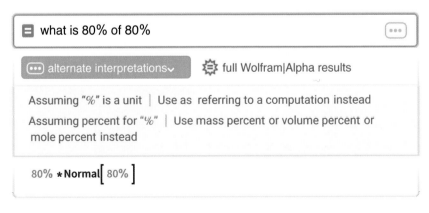

64%

When calculations use a unit of measurement, the Wolfram Language version of the calculation specifies this. In this case, mousing over "80%" shows Wolfram|Alpha Notebook Edition understands percentages and treats them as pieces of built-in knowledge.

Multiple calculations can be performed at one time, including taking a percentage of an integer, then taking a percentage of that result. The following example calculates 80% of 10 first, then calculates 50% of that result as the second calculation.

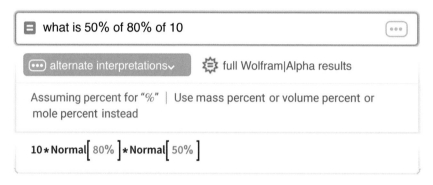

4

So far in this chapter, the symbols used in various calculations have all been available on a standard keyboard. For certain calculations involving other symbols like degrees, square roots or cube roots, the **Special Characters** menu can be used to represent those concepts. The button to display the **Special Characters** menu is located at the upper-right corner of the notebook, and after clicking it, a collection of available characters and symbols is displayed at the top of the notebook.

It is usually possible to describe a calculation in everyday English and calculate the desired result, but using the symbol for a square root is a more compact format and more closely mirrors the discussion about square roots in textbooks.

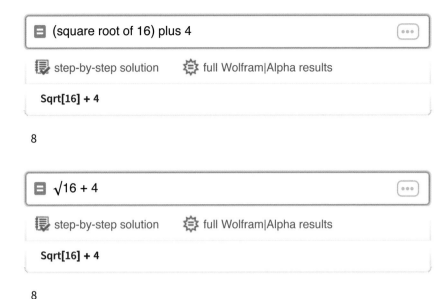

8

8

So far in this chapter, the full Wolfram|Alpha results have been shown for just one calculation, but notice most of the calculations also include this option. This can be a useful perspective for many types of calculations.

In addition to operations on different types of numbers, the software can also test properties of numbers, including testing whether a number is prime, finding the divisibility of numbers and searching for the divisors of a number.

Divisibility can be calculated in the form of a yes-or-no question, and for these types of calculations, the result is either true or false.

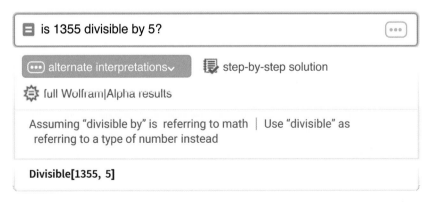

True

This test for divisibility can also be performed based on a list of possible divisors using parentheses to represent a list. The result is a new list containing values of true or false, corresponding to the values in the initial list. In this case, the result shows 1,355 is not divisible by 3, and 1,355 is divisible by 5.

{False, True, False, False}

Instead of querying for divisibility for specific numbers, using the phrase "divisors" creates a list of all integers where 30 is divisible by that integer.

{1, 2, 3, 5, 6, 10, 15, 30}

The result above is a list of numbers, and Wolfram|Alpha Notebook Edition uses curly brackets instead of parentheses to represent a list of numbers.

In addition to returning a list of divisors, a calculation can test whether a certain number is prime. When the calculation is posed as a yes-or-no question, the result is either true or false. The following calculation shows that 555 is not a prime number.

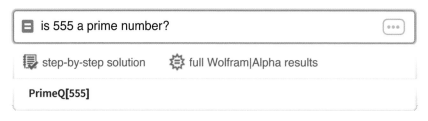

False

Wolfram|Alpha Notebook Edition has extensive data on prime numbers, and can also return a list of prime numbers or a certain prime number. The following example returns a query for the 43rd prime number, which is 191.

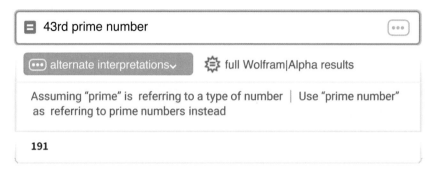

191

The included data can be used to query the largest known prime number as well.

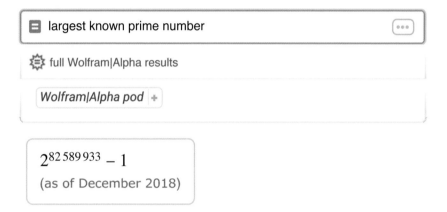

 Calculations can accept surprisingly large numbers and test whether that number is prime, including numbers in the hundreds of billions.

In addition to specific prime numbers, a calculation can also query a list of prime numbers, like the first 50 prime numbers.

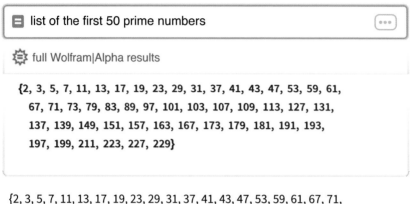

{2, 3, 5, 7, 11, 13, 17, 19, 23, 29, 31, 37, 41, 43, 47, 53, 59, 61, 67, 71, 73, 79, 83, 89, 97, 101, 103, 107, 109, 113, 127, 131, 137, 139, 149, 151, 157, 163, 167, 173, 179, 181, 191, 193, 197, 199, 211, 223, 227, 229}

For many types of problems, a series of calculations is often useful to solve the problem in steps. So far in this chapter, the calculations have been related to a common topic, but the calculations have not been related to each other. However, a calculation involving adding together the first 50 prime numbers and testing whether that total is prime is easier to visualize in steps. The phrase "that" refers to the last calculation in a notebook, and is a useful approach for a series of calculations to solve this problem.

The following calculation totals the previous result, which is the first 50 prime numbers.

5117

A calculation with the phrase "that" will always refer to the result of the last calculation, so the phrase can be used again to test whether the previous result is a prime number.

is that prime?

step-by-step solution     full Wolfram|Alpha results

**PrimeQ[5117]**

False

The final result of false means the total of the first 50 prime numbers is not a prime number.

This approach of referencing the last calculation works well when the calculations are evaluated in sequence. If one of the calculations is changed, it is often useful to reevaluate the entire sequence of calculations to make sure the term "that" refers to the updated previous result.

Calculations can also contain absolute values, either specified in everyday English or with typesetting that more closely resembles a discussion in a textbook.

absolute value of −5

step-by-step solution     full Wolfram|Alpha results

**Abs[−5]**

5

The absolute value symbol is available on a standard keyboard by pressing the Shift key with the \ key.

|−5| + 5

step-by-step solution     full Wolfram|Alpha results

**Abs[−5] + 5**

10

## Order of Operations

Calculations in a notebook can test order of operations, or use of parentheses can specify the order of operations. In the following calculation, the addition is performed prior to the multiplication.

35

In addition to an asterisk, a space can also be used in calculations to represent multiplication.

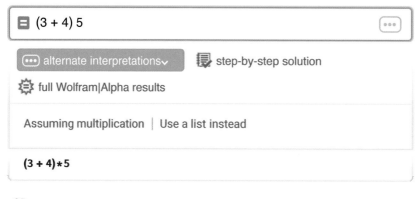

35

When the parentheses are moved such that the multiplication step is calculated prior to the addition step, the result changes as expected.

23

Without any parentheses, the calculation will follow typical conventions for the order of operations. In this case, the multiplication is performed first and the addition is performed second.

 For demonstration purposes, the calculations in this chapter are small numbers, but Wolfram|Alpha Notebook Edition has a powerful engine and can work with very large numbers too.

3 + 4 * 5

3 + 4*5

23

For more intricate examples with multiple steps of addition and multiplication, reviewing the steps performed in the calculation is often just as useful as the final result. The **step-by-step solution** button can be used to create a new calculation with a step-by-step solution.

3 + 4 * 5 * 3 + 7 − 6/2

3 + 4*5*3 + 7 − 6/2

67

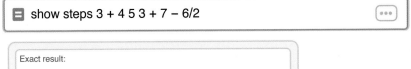

show steps 3 + 4 5 3 + 7 − 6/2

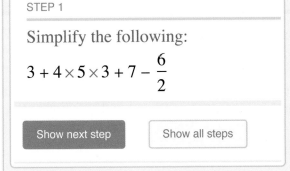

Exact result:

STEP 1

Simplify the following:

$$3 + 4 \times 5 \times 3 + 7 - \frac{6}{2}$$

Show next step    Show all steps

The formatting for step-by-step solutions is uniform across all types of calculations. By default, the first step is shown, which is often a restatement of the original problem. The **Show next step** button can be used to display steps one at a time, which gives the user a chance to compare their thought process to the solution in the software. The **Show all steps** button will display all steps at any point, which is a useful way to compare a manually calculated solution to the solution in the software.

## Basics of Variables in Algebra

While calculations in a notebook can provide insight into order of operations using specific numeric values, the software also understands variables and symbols. This means calculations involving order of operations can be generalized using algebraic expressions.

The following calculation tests equality for two algebraic expressions.

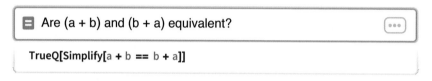

True

This overall approach can be used for more sophisticated algebraic expressions to test order of operations and algebraic equality.

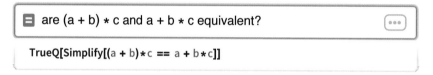

False

 Any letter can be used as a symbol in algebraic calculations. The software does not require use of only *a*, *b* and *c*.

Calculations can also be stated algebraically with variables, and specific numerical values can be substituted for the variables to calculate a numerical result based on those specific values.

2(x + y) where x = 3 and y = 4

2*(x + y) /. {x –> 3, y –> 4}

14

In general, calculations in a notebook will automatically simplify expressions, including algebraic expressions. A calculation using the variable $x$ will be simplified in the result.

2x + x + 5x

2*x + x + 5*x

$8x$

This simplification will be performed in an algebraic expression with one variable or multiple variables. In the following calculation $a$ and $b$ are used as variables instead of $x$.

4b + 6 + 2b + 12 − 6 + 2a

4*b + 6 + 2*b + 12 − 6 + 2*a

$12 + 2a + 6b$

A simplified expression in the output might eliminate variables entirely. In addition to using $a$, $b$ or $x$ as variables, the **Special Characters** menu can be used to enter Greek characters as variables. In the following calculation, the Greek character beta ($\beta$) is used, and the simplified expression eliminates $\beta$.

$(2\beta + \beta) / (4\beta)$

$(2*\beta + \beta)/(4*\beta)$

$$\frac{3}{4}$$

Several other common characters are available in the **Special Characters** menu like alpha ($\alpha$) and theta ($\theta$), which can also be used as symbols.

## Solving Equations

When working with equations that include one or more variables, solving the equation for a certain variable is a very common operation. The term "solve" can be used to solve an equation, mirroring how this calculation is commonly stated in everyday English.

---

▤ solve 3x + 3 = 15 for x    ⟨•••⟩

Solve[3 * x + 3 == 15, x]

---

$\{\{x \to 4\}\}$

Calculations can use several different phrases for solving equations, and in this case, it is not necessary to specify the variable name in a calculation. When that phrase is eliminated, the calculation automatically recognizes the variable name in the algebraic expression and solves for that variable.

---

▤ solve (3x + 3)/3 = 15    ⟨•••⟩

Solve$\left[(3 * x + 3)/3 == 15, x\right]$

---

$\{\{x \to 14\}\}$

Multiple symbols and variables can be used when solving equations. In this case, the algebraic expression does not contain integers for the coefficients, and instead includes symbols $a$, $b$ and $c$. The expression can be solved for $x$, and the result is given in terms of these symbols.

---

▤ solve a * x^2 + b * x + c = 0 for x    ⟨•••⟩

Solve[a * x^2 + b * x + c == 0, x, MaxExtraConditions -> Automatic]

---

$$\left\{\left\{x \to \frac{-\sqrt{b^2 - 4ac} - b}{2a}\right\}, \left\{x \to \frac{\sqrt{b^2 - 4ac} - b}{2a}\right\}\right\}$$

The **Special Characters** menu can provide Greek characters that act as variables in an algebraic expression as well as symbols like $\pi$, which is a special character with a known value. The following calculation does not specify the equation should be solved for $\beta$, but the software automatically recognizes $\beta$ as the variable and returns a result using exact values of $\pi$.

solve $\pi \beta + 7 = \pi$   •••

Solve[Pi * $\beta$ + 7 == Pi, $\beta$]

$$\left\{\left\{\beta \rightarrow \frac{\pi - 7}{\pi}\right\}\right\}$$

 As mentioned earlier in the chapter, either an asterisk or a space can be used to represent multiplication in a calculation.

In addition to the term "that," the term "result" also refers to the output for the previous calculation. The following calculation takes the last result, which uses exact values of $\pi$, and provides a decimal approximation to 10 digits.

result rounded to 10 digits   •••

N[{{$\beta$ -> (−7 + Pi) / Pi}}, 10]

$\{\{\beta \rightarrow -1.228169203\}\}$

## Visualization of Numbers

Calculations in a notebook can include a wide variety of graphics, and visualizing numbers on a number line is one possible type of visualization that is useful in prealgebra.

The phrase "on a number line" will format the result as a number line.

−5 and 3 on a number line   •••

NumberLinePlot[{−5, 3}]

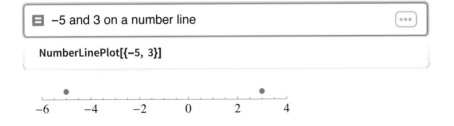

In addition to visualizing integers, number lines can provide a visualization for decimals with varying quantities of digits.

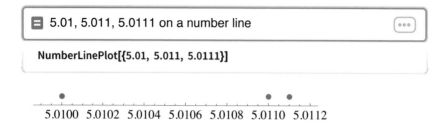

5.01, 5.011, 5.0111 on a number line

NumberLinePlot[{5.01, 5.011, 5.0111}]

Mathematical constants like $\pi$, entered with the **Special Characters** menu at the upper right of the notebook, can be used in calculations involving a number line.

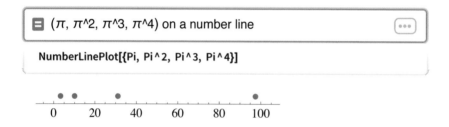

$(\pi, \pi^2, \pi^3, \pi^4)$ on a number line

NumberLinePlot[{Pi, Pi^2, Pi^3, Pi^4}]

Use of parentheses is not required for the previous calculation, but is often a clearer format for a calculation when reading through the notebook at a later time.

In addition to number lines, a calculation using coordinates will be displayed using the coordinate system when the term "graph" is used. The following calculation is a graph based on an $(x, y)$ pair.

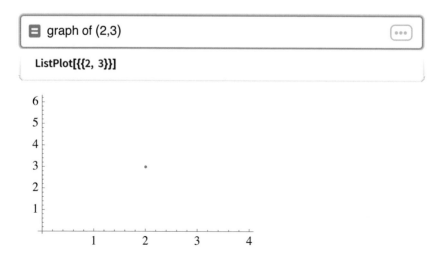

graph of (2,3)

ListPlot[{{2, 3}}]

Different quadrants of the coordinate system can be visualized by using negative values in the $(x, y)$ pair.

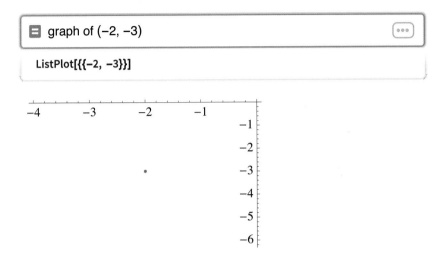

A graph of multiple $(x, y)$ points can be visualized on the same set of axes.

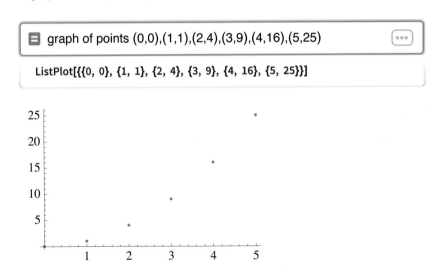

In addition to creating a graph of certain points in the coordinate system, calculations can take the next step and return a visualization of the line that connects the two points. This can be calculated in two steps. The first calculation finds the equation of the line, and the second calculation creates a graph of that equation.

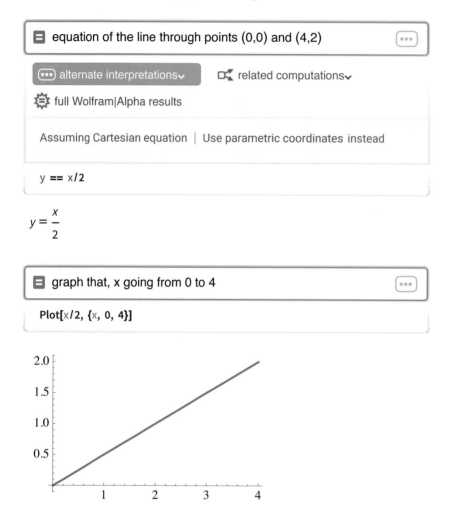

This calculation also happens to be a nice example where the full Wolfram|Alpha results provide a good alternate graph as well as some useful related calculations.

## Working with Money

Several examples in this chapter use the knowledge that is built into Wolfram|Alpha Notebook Edition. The software contains extensive knowledge of units of measurement, which includes knowledge of currencies.

A calculation can specify money as a unit, and the result will be in terms of that same unit. Since the result of the following calculation is a portion of a dollar, the software uses cents as the unit of measurement for the result.

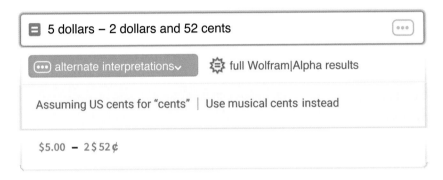

248.¢

Instead of letting Wolfram|Alpha Notebook Edition decide units for the result, a calculation can specify the unit. The following calculation uses the phrase "in dollars" to convert the result to US dollars instead of cents.

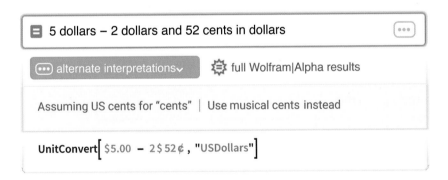

$2.48

In addition to US currency, a calculation can include US dollars as well as Canadian dollars.

C$4.86

 Wolfram|Alpha Notebook Edition has built-in data for units of measurement that are constant over time, like feet or miles, but the software also understands current exchange rates. The result above will likely be different over time as exchange rates change.

Similar to a previous calculation in this chapter, including the phrase "in USD" will convert the result to US dollars instead of returning the result in Canadian dollars.

$3.54

Japanese yen is also an available unit for calculations.

$5.93

When using units, the software understands these units across many calculations, and units are tightly integrated into the software. Calculating a percent of five US dollars is one possible calculation.

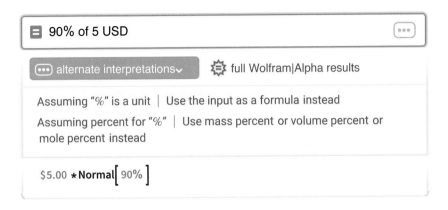

$4.50

When multiple calculations are included in a single input cell, the result is returned in list format.

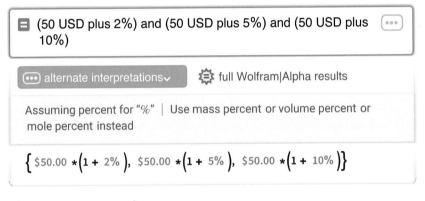

{$51.00, $52.50, $55.00}

 The term "and" can be used to specify a list of values, or a comma can be used to separate the three values. The result is identical for either phrasing.

This list of three values in US dollars can be visualized in a graph using the term "that" to specify the previous result.

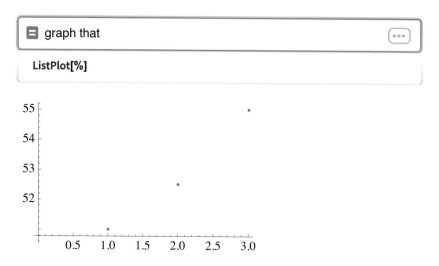

## Conclusion

Wolfram|Alpha Notebook Edition provides a unified environment to explore many concepts in prealgebra. Comparing calculations involving algebraic calculations, different forms of numbers, various types of graphs and step-by-step solutions all in one unified notebook can provide useful insights. Notebooks also act as a nice archive for explorations of concepts for later review.

## Exercises

1. Calculate $71.877 - 3.38$.

2. Calculate $-64 / 8$.

3. Calculate the square root of 121.

4. Calculate 15% of 85 as a decimal.

5. Calculate $(-16)\wedge2$.

6. Calculate 3 feet + 17 inches.

7. Calculate 5,000 yen + \$10 + 10 euros in USD.

8. Solve $n - 3 = -15$ for $n$.

9. Solve $2x + 8 < 14$ for $x$.

10. Graph and find the slope of the following line: $y = 5x + 9$.

# CHAPTER 12

# Algebra in Wolfram|Alpha Notebook Edition

## Introduction

The notebook environment in Wolfram|Alpha Notebook Edition is useful for solving equations, changing the form of equations and graphing equations, all in one unified document to explore concepts in algebra. Step-by-step solutions are also useful to check mechanics when solving problems in algebra to get real-time feedback. Many types of calculations and visualizations are possible in the software, and this chapter will outline a useful subset to act as a guide for exploring concepts in algebra.

## Basic Algebraic Operations

Calculations in a notebook will automatically simplify algebraic expressions, and if a calculation contains a factored polynomial, the result will be the same factored form of the equation.

$(a + 5)(a + 9)$

To expand an equation into polynomial form, the term "expand" can be used.

$a^2 + 14a + 45$

An equation can include symbols instead of integers for a calculation to expand an equation into polynomial form.

$$a^2 + ab + ac + bc$$

While the characters *a*, *b*, *c*, *d*, *x* and *y* are commonly used to outline algebraic concepts, the software will accept any character as a symbol in algebraic calculations. The **Special Characters** menu also provides additional Greek characters that can be used as symbols in equations.

The **step-by-step solution** button creates a new pair of input and output cells to show the mechanics for expanding this equation. In this case, the solution involves the FOIL method, and step-by-step solutions follow a typical textbook explanation for solving this type of problem. Step-by-step solutions can be displayed one step at a time, or all of the steps can be displayed at one time.

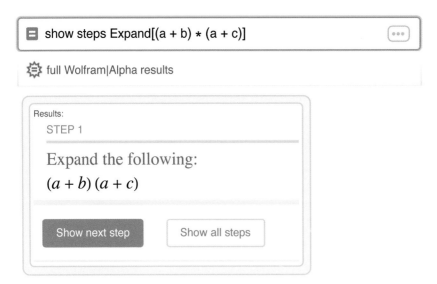

A polynomial using symbols instead of numbers can also be computed into factored form using the term "factor" in the input cell.

factor a^2 + ab + ac + bc

Factor[a^2 + a*b + a*c + b*c]

$(a + b)(a + c)$

 The result uses a space to represent multiplication. In calculations, either an asterisk or space can be used to represent multiplication. But in the calculation above, Wolfram|Alpha Notebook Edition makes the assumption that "ab" is "a" times "b" even without the space.

The term "together" can be used to put terms in a sum over a common denominator.

together 1/(x + 1) + 1/(x − 1)

Together[1/(x + 1) + 1/(x − 1)]

$$\frac{2x}{(-1 + x)(1 + x)}$$

Conversely, the term "apart" can be used to rewrite an equation as a sum of terms with minimal denominators.

apart 2x / ((−1 + x)(1 + x))

Apart[2*(x/((-1 + x)*(1 + x)))]

$$\frac{1}{x + 1} + \frac{1}{x - 1}$$

 Calculations in Wolfram|Alpha Notebook Edition can include extra spaces as well, which is sometimes a handy way to make a complicated equation easier to read. In the calculations above, an extra space is added to separate the terms and the calculation still returns the expected result.

When working with equations and different forms of an equation, creating various graphs can often give a useful perspective. The term "that" can be used in any calculation to reference the previous result, and in this case creates a graph of the equation in the previous result.

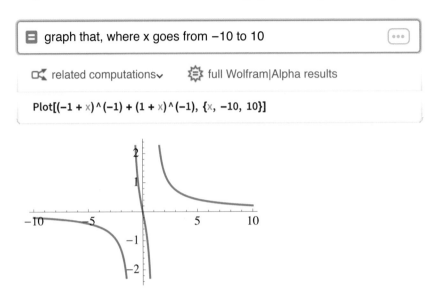

graph that, where x goes from −10 to 10

related computations∨    full Wolfram|Alpha results

Plot[(−1 + x)^(−1) + (1 + x)^(−1), {x, −10, 10}]

Calculations can also collect terms to factor common terms out.

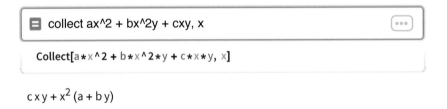

collect ax^2 + bx^2y + cxy, x

Collect[a∗x^2 + b∗x^2∗y + c∗x∗y, x]

$cxy + x^2(a + by)$

## Radicals

Radicals, like square roots, can be described in everyday English in calculations.

square root of x^2

Sqrt[x^2]

$\sqrt{x^2}$

In addition to using everyday English, the **Special Characters** menu at the upper-right corner of a notebook can be used to enter a square root symbol that more closely mirrors textbook notation. This formatting is often preferred to make the calculation more concise.

$\sqrt{x^2}$

The result above demonstrates that Wolfram|Alpha Notebook Edition can solve problems across many levels of math, including complex numbers. In introductory courses, it might be useful to add an assumption that $x$ is greater than 0 to the calculation to simplify the radial.

$x$

Instead of using a variable, a calculation can involve specific numbers within radicals, including a cube root.

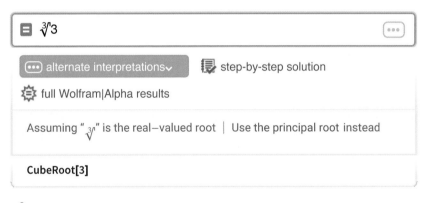

$\sqrt[3]{3}$

Wolfram|Alpha Notebook Edition always provides results in exact form, if possible. The term "that" can be used to reference the previous result in a new calculation to calculate a decimal approximation.

```
☰  approximate that                          ⋯
```
```
    N[%]
```

1.44225

The calculation above used an integer; when a calculation starts with a decimal approximation, the calculation is no longer exact, and a decimal approximation is returned in the result. This overall convention can be used to calculate a result in decimal format for a wide variety of calculations.

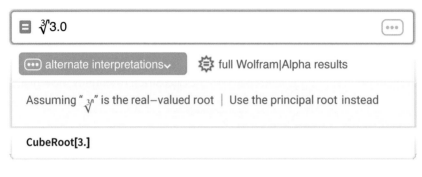

1.44225

The term "simplify" can be used to simplify expressions that contain radicals.

$4\sqrt{x}$

Simplification of an expression can be performed with specific numerical values rather than variables.

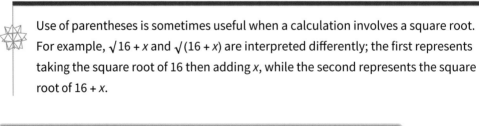

Use of parentheses is sometimes useful when a calculation involves a square root. For example, $\sqrt{16} + x$ and $\sqrt{(16 + x)}$ are interpreted differently; the first represents taking the square root of 16 then adding $x$, while the second represents the square root of $16 + x$.

$\dfrac{\sqrt{15}}{4}$

The **step-by-step solution** button for the previous calculation creates a new pair of input and output cells to show the steps for this simplification. Earlier in this chapter, a step-by-step solution was shown to expand an equation, and the steps to simplify an expression with a radial are much different. Step-by-step solutions in the software contain a large variety of solutions and automatically identify the type of problem to provide an explanation for the solution that mirrors a typical textbook.

For any supported step-by-step solution, the buttons are the same to work through the solution one step at a time or show all the steps at once. The steps themselves and the quantity of steps will differ with different problems, but the buttons and formatting will always look the same.

## Absolute Value

Calculations using an absolute value can be entered using everyday English or more typical notation found in a textbook.

11

The typeset notation for absolute value can be entered on a typical keyboard by pressing the Shift key with the \ key.

−|7| + 5 + |−3|

step-by-step solution    full Wolfram|Alpha results

−Abs[7] + 5 + Abs[−3]

1

Calculations can use variables with absolute values to simplify algebraic expressions.

|3a| + 5a − 6 + |2a|

step-by-step solution    full Wolfram|Alpha results

Abs[3∗a] + 5∗a − 6 + Abs[2∗a]

$5|a| + 5a - 6$

The term "result" can be used to reference the previous result and substitute a value of −1 for the variable $a$ in the equation.

result where a = −1

full Wolfram|Alpha results

−6 + 5∗a + 5∗Abs[a] /. {a −> −1}

−6

Both the terms "that" and "result" can be used to reference the previous calculation, and the user can choose the phrase that makes sense in the context of the calculations.

# Equation Solving

The term "solve" can be used for a wide variety of problems involving solving equations with one or more variables. When solving an equation with one variable, it is not necessary to specify the variable using the phrase "for x," but either phrasing will produce the desired result.

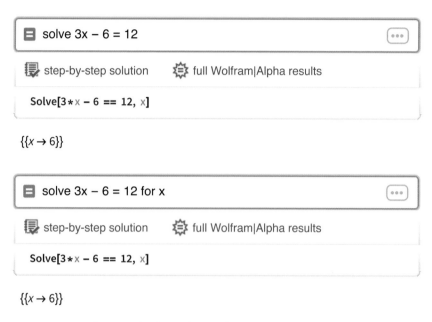

solve 3x − 6 = 12

step-by-step solution    full Wolfram|Alpha results

Solve[3*x − 6 == 12, x]

$\{\{x \to 6\}\}$

solve 3x − 6 = 12 for x

step-by-step solution    full Wolfram|Alpha results

Solve[3*x − 6 == 12, x]

$\{\{x \to 6\}\}$

Equations involving radicals can be used when solving for a particular variable.

solve 3x − $\sqrt{5}$ = 12

Solve[3*x − Sqrt[5] == 12, x]

$$\left\{\left\{x \to \frac{1}{3}\left(12 + \sqrt{5}\right)\right\}\right\}$$

To approximate the result, the term "result" can be used to reference the previous result and round it to 10 digits.

result rounded to 10 digits

N[{{x −> (12 + Sqrt[5])/3}}, 10]

$\{\{x \to 4.745355992\}\}$

Results sometimes contain radicals as well to represent the solution as an exact value.

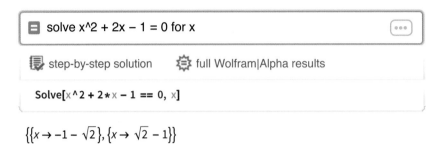

> ⊟  solve x^2 + 2x − 1 = 0 for x                    ⋯
>
> 📋 step-by-step solution    ⚙ full Wolfram|Alpha results
>
> Solve[x^2 + 2*x − 1 == 0, x]

$$\{\{x \to -1 - \sqrt{2}\}, \{x \to \sqrt{2} - 1\}\}$$

When the result contains more than one solution, the output cell separates the solutions with curly brackets. The term "result" still refers to the set of solutions rather than one or the other solution, and the solutions can be rounded to five digits with one calculation.

> ⊟  result rounded to 5 digits                    ⋯
>
> N[{{x −> −1 − Sqrt[2]}, {x −> −1 + Sqrt[2]}}, 5]

$$\{\{x \to -2.4142\}, \{x \to 0.41421\}\}$$

When a calculation includes two equations with two variables, the systems of equations are solved for both variables.

> ⊟  solve 2x + 4y = 14 and x − y = 4                    ⋯
>
> Solve[{2*x + 4*y == 14, x − y == 4}, {x, y}]

$$\{\{x \to 5, y \to 1\}\}$$

When the result is not an integer, by default an exact result will be given using fractions.

> ⊟  solve 3x + 5y = 15 and x − y = 3                    ⋯
>
> 📋 step-by-step solution    ⚙ full Wolfram|Alpha results
>
> Solve[{3*x + 5*y == 15, x − y == 3}, {x, y}]

$$\left\{\left\{x \to \frac{15}{4}, y \to \frac{3}{4}\right\}\right\}$$

Two equations with two variables can also be solved in terms of symbol *a* when that symbol is used in the equations.

solve x + a = 10 and x − 2y = 4

step-by-step solution    full Wolfram|Alpha results

**Solve[{x + a == 10, x − 2\*y == 4}, {x, y}]**

$$\left\{\left\{x \rightarrow 10 - a, y \rightarrow \frac{6 - a}{2}\right\}\right\}$$

 In the previous calculation, even with three symbols, Wolfram|Alpha Notebook Edition recognizes that *x* and *y* are the most commonly used variables and solves for both *x* and *y*.

At times, one of the equations might not include both variables, and in this case, the solution is still provided for both *x* and *y*.

solve 3x + 5y = 15 and x = 3

step-by-step solution    full Wolfram|Alpha results

**Solve[{3\*x + 5\*y == 15, x == 3}, {x, y}]**

$$\left\{\left\{x \rightarrow 3, y \rightarrow \frac{6}{5}\right\}\right\}$$

Step-by-step solutions are a useful component in Wolfram|Alpha Notebook Edition, and step-by-step solutions are available for algebraic calculations like solving equations. After clicking the **step-by-step solution** button in the previous input cell, a new pair of input and output cells are displayed with that step-by-step solution.

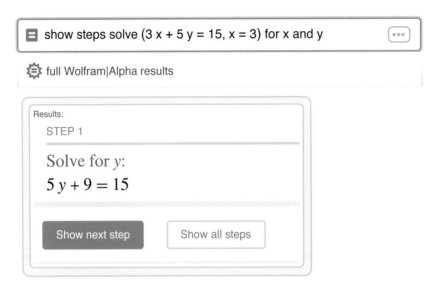

This chapter will often show only the first step of a step-by-step solution, but the progression of steps is unique based on each type of calculation. In this case, the various steps make sense for solving equations, and might involve a much longer series of steps compared to calculations earlier in the chapter involving order of operations.

 As mentioned in a previous chapter, step-by-step solutions are live calculations and do not draw from a predefined list of solved problems. So there are many, many possible variations in step-by-step solutions.

The software can solve equations that use a greater-than symbol instead of an equal sign.

$x < -7$

Wolfram|Alpha Notebook Edition contains a sophisticated solver for equations, and a single calculation can include multiple radicals or more intricate equations.

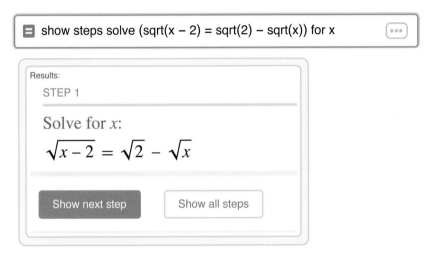

$$\{\{x \to 2\}\}$$

The step-by-step solution to solve this equation provides unique steps to simplify the terms with a radical. While it is common to enter a calculation first and then click the **step-by-step solution** button to show steps, any new input cell can contain the phrase "show steps" directly to generate the step-by-step solution.

show steps solve (sqrt(x − 2) = sqrt(2) − sqrt(x)) for x

Results:

STEP 1

Solve for $x$:
$$\sqrt{x-2} = \sqrt{2} - \sqrt{x}$$

| Show next step | Show all steps |

There are seven steps outlined in this particular solution, including several to navigate and simplify the terms with radicals.

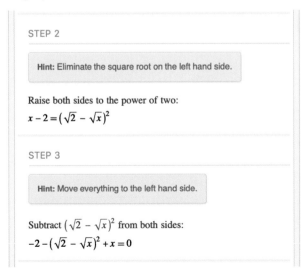

# Graphing and Lines

Wolfram|Alpha Notebook Edition supports a wide variety of different types of graphs, as well as the ability to graph a wide variety of equations.

A number line can be used to visualize values for various numbers involving radicals.

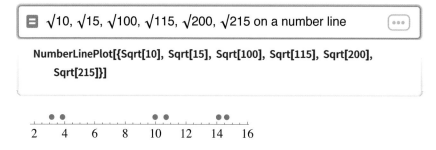

Use of the phrase "number line" at the beginning of the calculations produces the same result as using that phrase at the end of a calculation. In addition, the phrase can even be shortened to just "line."

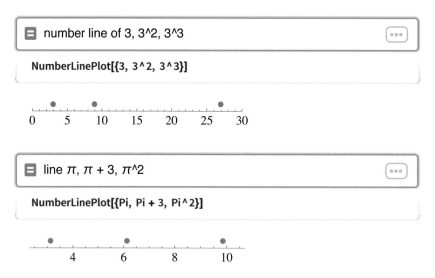

In addition to a list of specific points, a number line can be used to visualize inequalities.

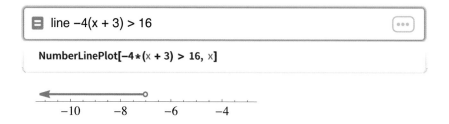

A number line can be used to graphically visualize solutions when solving an equation with inequalities. The first calculation provides the solution in algebraic form; the second provides the solution in graphical form.

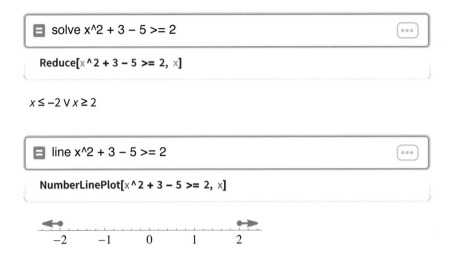

solve x^2 + 3 − 5 >= 2

Reduce[x^2 + 3 − 5 >= 2, x]

$x \leq -2 \vee x \geq 2$

line x^2 + 3 − 5 >= 2

NumberLinePlot[x^2 + 3 − 5 >= 2, x]

Notice the number line has a solid dot when that point is included in the inequality (>=), and an open dot when that point is not included in the inequality (>).

The term "graph" is also a very flexible term to visualize a wide variety of equations, including equations in slope-intercept form.

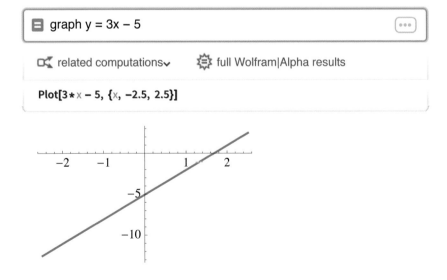

graph y = 3x − 5

related computations⌄    full Wolfram|Alpha results

Plot[3*x − 5, {x, −2.5, 2.5}]

In addition to creating a graph, the software includes knowledge about algebraic concepts and can be used to directly query the slope for a particular equation.

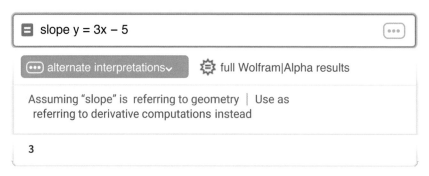

To visualize variations in slope, the variable *m* can be used to represent slope in a calculation that produces a graph, with *m* varying from −5 to 5. Use of the term "varying" creates a mouse-driven model to adjust the parameter and visualize the effects on the graph in real time. Other parameters for the *x* and *y* axes help to keep the view of the graph the same when moving the slider, which is often desirable for an animation.

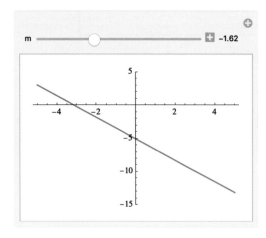

Throughout this book, different variations of phrasing have been used to specify the domain and range for a graph (the values for the $x$ and $y$ axes). While the software often chooses useful values automatically, the graph above specifies values for both the $x$ and $y$ axes. This can be specified on any type of graph, not just this animation.

The $y$ intercept is also a common concept to query in an equation, and can be queried directly.

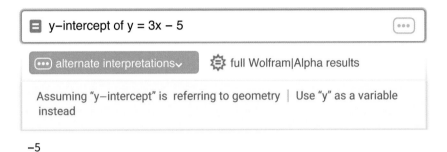

−5

Similar to a previous example, use of the term "varying" with the symbol $b$ changes that value and adjusts the graph in real time based on those changes to the equation. The slider shows variations from −5 to 5 to easily visualize where the line intercepts the $y$ axis for many specific cases.

> graph y = 3 x + b, x going from −5 to 5, y going from −15 to 15, varying b from −5 to 5

Manipulate[Plot[3∗x + b, {x, −5, 5}, PlotRange −> {−15, 15}], {{b, 0}, −5, 5, Appearance −> "Labeled"}]

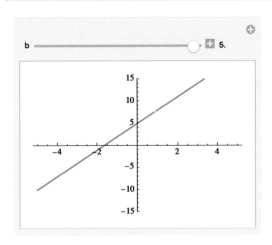

A calculation to determine the $x$ intercept of an equation is possible as well since Wolfram|Alpha Notebook Edition understands this overall concept through its built-in knowledge. This solution can be compared to explicitly solving the equation where $y$ equals 0 to reinforce this concept.

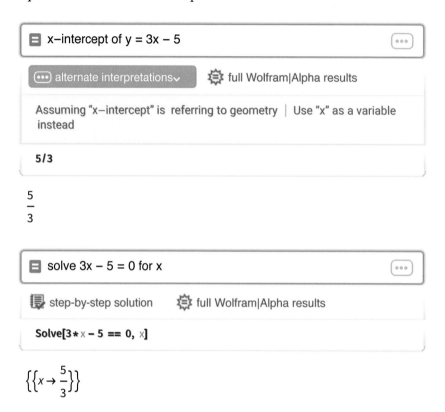

> ▤ x–intercept of y = 3x – 5                    ⋯
>
> ⋯ alternate interpretations⌄    ⚙ full Wolfram|Alpha results
>
> Assuming "x–intercept" is referring to geometry │ Use "x" as a variable instead
>
> 5/3

$$\frac{5}{3}$$

> ▤ solve 3x – 5 = 0 for x                    ⋯
>
> 📑 step-by-step solution    ⚙ full Wolfram|Alpha results
>
> Solve[3 * x – 5 == 0, x]

$$\left\{\left\{x \to \frac{5}{3}\right\}\right\}$$

"Solve" can also be used explicitly to change the form of an equation to $y = mx + b$ form.

> ▤ solve 3x + 5y = 11 for y                    ⋯
>
> ⚙ full Wolfram|Alpha results
>
> Solve[3 * x + 5 * y == 11, y, MaxExtraConditions –> Automatic]

$$\left\{\left\{y \to \frac{11}{5} - \frac{3x}{5}\right\}\right\}$$

So far in this chapter, the coefficients in the equations have been integers, but Wolfram|Alpha Notebook Edition can work with equations where coefficients are fractions as well.

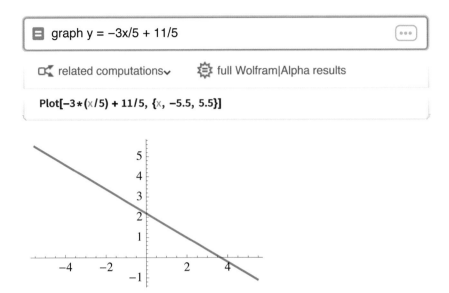

Coefficients with decimals work identically as well.

The built-in knowledge in Wolfram|Alpha Notebook Edition can identify the slope, the $x$ intercept and the $y$ intercept in an equation, whether that equation is in slope-intercept form or in an alternate form.

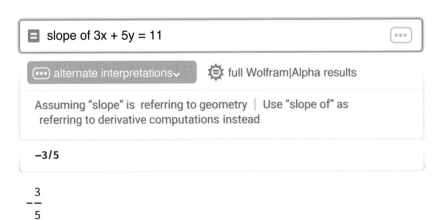

$$\frac{3}{5}$$

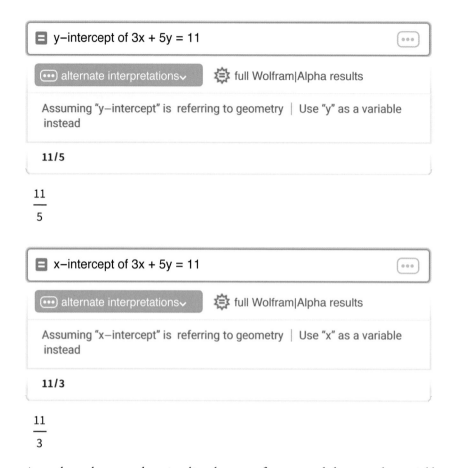

A graph can be created to visualize the curve for a second-degree polynomial by using exactly the same phrase "graph" in the calculation.

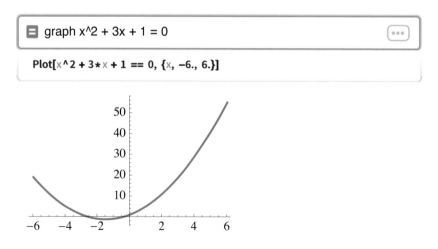

An additional phrase can be added at the end of a calculation to specify lower and upper bounds for the $x$ axis on the graph. In the following calculation, the $x$ axis will be displayed from $-4$ to $1$ to provide a useful view of the points where the curve crosses the $x$ axis.

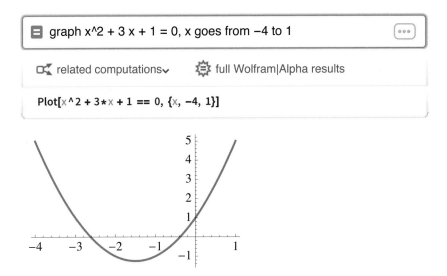

This is one of many cases where a graph can support an understanding of an algebraic concept, and solving the equation for $x$ returns the specific values where the curve crosses the $x$ axis.

⊟  solve x^2 + 3x + 1 = 0 for x                                     ⚫⚫⚫

📋 step-by-step solution          ⚙ full Wolfram|Alpha results

  Solve[x^2 + 3*x + 1 == 0, x]

$$\left\{\left\{x \to \frac{1}{2}\left(-3 - \sqrt{5}\right)\right\}, \left\{x \to \frac{1}{2}\left(\sqrt{5} - 3\right)\right\}\right\}$$

The result can be approximated to help with visual comparison with the graph.

⊟  result to 5 digits                                               ⚫⚫⚫

⚙ full Wolfram|Alpha results

  N[{{x -> (-3 - Sqrt[5])/2}, {x -> (-3 + Sqrt[5])/2}}, 5]

$$\{\{x \to -2.6180\}, \{x \to -0.38197\}\}$$

When a calculation has more than one result, the results are separated by curly brackets to represent the list of solutions.

Use of the term "varying" also creates a mouse-driven model for other types of equations. The following example varies the symbol $b$ from 1 to 10 to show the effect of varying that parameter on the graph in real time.

graph x^2 + 3 x + b = 0, x goes from −4 to 1, y goes from −5 to 15, vary b from 1 to 10

Manipulate[Plot[x^2 + 3*x + b == 0, {x, −4, 1}, PlotRange −> {−5, 15}],
{{b, 11/2}, 1, 10, Appearance −> "Labeled"}]

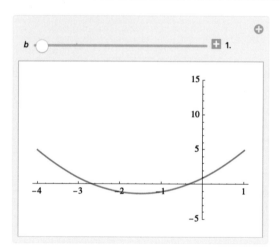

This overall approach can be used to visualize horizontal stretch as well. Rather than varying the third term of the equation, the following example varies the coefficient to the $x^2$ term. The model shows the resulting graph when this parameter is varied in real time, showing the horizontal stretches and compressions.

graph bx^2 + 3 x + 1 = 0, x goes from −4 to 2, y goes from −5 to 15, vary b from 1 to 10

Manipulate[Plot[b∗x^2 + 3∗x + 1 == 0, {x, −4, 2},
     PlotRange −> {−5, 15}], {{b, 11/2}, 1, 10, Appearance −> "Labeled"}]

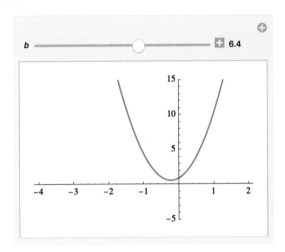

 The text of this book uses 2D typesetting for $x^2$, while the calculation uses "x^2" with a caret. This mirrors what is currently possible in Wolfram|Alpha Notebook Edition where the **Writing Assistant** palette can be used to create exponents in text for formulas, but calculations do not currently support this level of typesetting.

## Working with Exponents

Exponents can be included in any type of calculation in a notebook, and Wolfram|Alpha Notebook Edition includes useful step-by-step solutions for common calculations involving exponents.

The caret symbol represents an exponent, similar to other software.

5^2 + 3^0

5^2 + 3^0

26

The **step-by-step solution** button produces a summary of how to solve arithmetic problems involving exponents.

Negative exponents can be used in calculations with similar notation.

8

The **step-by-step solution** button confirms the negative exponent represents one over the value, and produces the steps to find the numeric result.

This book often shows only the first step of a step-by-step solution, but the reader should enter the calculations as they read these chapters and work through the step-by-step solutions individually to get a feel for the results for different types of problems.

Exponents in equations can be used when calculating the expanded form.

expand (x + 1)^2 + (x − 1)

Expand[(x + 1)^2 + (x − 1)]

$$x^2 + 3x$$

Simplifying the previous result returns an expression with common terms factored out.

simplify that

Simplify[3*x + x^2]

$$x(x + 3)$$

The entire process of expanding the expression and factoring out common terms is outlined in more detail in the step-by-step solutions.

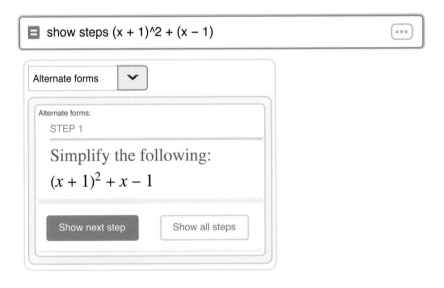

show steps (x + 1)^2 + (x − 1)

Alternate forms

Alternate forms:
STEP 1

Simplify the following:

$$(x + 1)^2 + x − 1$$

Show next step      Show all steps

A calculation with a natural logarithm can be stated through the use of the common convention of $\ln(x)$.

ln(10) to 100 digits

N[Log[10], 100]

2.3025850929940456840179914546843642076011014886287729760333279009675726 0ˑˑ.
9677352480235997205089598298

 It is necessary to specify the phrase "to 100 digits" in this calculation; otherwise, the result will be the same as the input for the calculation. The decimal approximations in this book tend to be a modest number of digits just to conserve screen space, but this calculation can easily be extended to one million digits instead of one hundred.

The term "graph" can create a graph based on many formats and types of equations, including an equation with a natural logarithm.

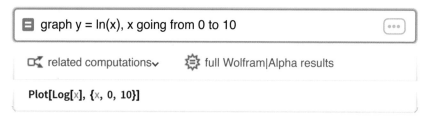

graph y = ln(x), x going from 0 to 10

related computations∨    full Wolfram|Alpha results

Plot[Log[x], {x, 0, 10}]

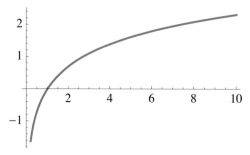

The term "varying" can be used to adjust the value of a coefficient in an equation involving a natural logarithm. In the following calculation, the symbol $b$ is varied from 1 to 10, and the graph is updated in real time based on the new equation.

graph y = ln(b x), x going from 0 to 10, y going from –5 to 5,
varying b from 1 to 10

```
Manipulate[Plot[Log[b*x], {x, 0, 10}, PlotRange -> {-5, 5}],
    {{b, 11/2}, 1, 10, Appearance -> "Labeled"}]
```

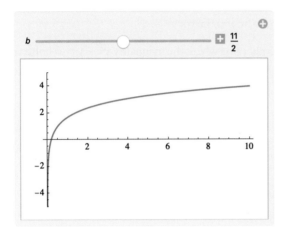

 In addition to moving the slider to adjust the value of the symbol *b*, clicking the plus icon displays a second row of buttons, including an input field to type in new values directly. This can be more precise than moving the slider at times.

## Conclusion

Concepts in algebra often involve comparing an algebraic solution to a graph, or working through many specific variations to understand a larger-picture concept. Notebooks are a useful format for a series of related calculations to compare different results, or algebraic solutions against various graphs. Mouse-driven models are also an effective way to visualize variations and focus on a larger-picture concept.

## Exercises

1. Calculate the expanded form of $(x - 1)(x - 2)(x - 3)(x - 4)(x - 5)$.

2. Create a plot of the polynomial in Exercise 1.

3. Create an interactive plot of $\sin(a x)$ for $x$ over the interval $[-\pi, \pi]$ that lets you vary the values of $a$ with a slider from 1 to 10.

4. Define the equation of a line with slope 3 and $y$ intercept 5.

5. Evaluate the cube root of $\dfrac{10\,648}{343}$.

6. Replace the answer from Exercise 5 with its approximate equivalent.

7. Calculate, using "solve," the value of $x$ for which the functions $x + 1$ and $x^2 - 2x + 1$ are equal.

8. Use step-by-step functionality to show how to factor $x^3 - a^6$.

9. Use "line" to find the region in the number line where the inequality $x^2 - 1 > 0$ holds true.

10. Write the step-by-step solutions for Exercise 7.

# CHAPTER 13
# Trigonometry and Precalculus in Wolfram|Alpha Notebook Edition

## Introduction

Trigonometry and precalculus are both areas where exploring many variations can greatly aid in understanding overall concepts. Notebooks are a convenient environment for individual calculations and graphics, or to create mouse-driven models to see many variations in real time to understand a broad concept. Wolfram|Alpha Notebook Edition is also useful for visualizations related to conic sections or polar coordinates, or exploring sequences of numbers. This chapter will outline a useful subset of calculations and visualizations to act as a guide for exploring concepts in trigonometry or precalculus.

## Trigonometry Functions

All trigonometric functions are built into Wolfram|Alpha Notebook Edition and can be used to calculate specific values. The degree symbol in the following calculation was entered using the **Special Characters** menu at the upper-right-hand side of the notebook.

> ▣ cos(90°) ⋯
>
> Cos[ 90° ]

0

> ▣ sin(90°) ⋯
>
> Sin[ 90° ]

1

Calculations can convert degrees to radians, or radians to degrees.

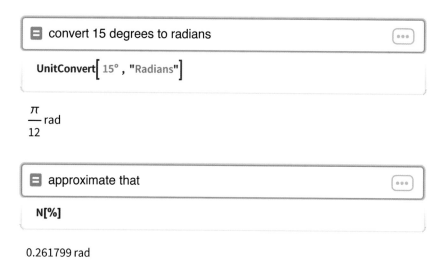

$$\frac{\pi}{12} \text{ rad}$$

0.261799 rad

More advanced trigonometric functions are also available. The following calculation approximates the cosecant of $5\pi/7$ to 10 digits.

1.279048008

---

The $\pi$ symbol was created using the **Special Characters** menu in the upper-right corner of the notebook.

When a specific trigonometric calculation is undefined, the result of the calculation is **ComplexInfinity**. Since degrees are not specified in the calculation involving a trigonometric function, the calculation automatically defaults to radians.

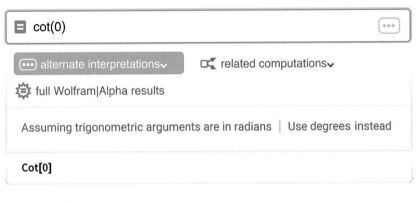

ComplexInfinity

While many algebraic equations will be simplified automatically during a calculation, the term "simplify" is used to apply trigonometric identities to an equation for simplification.

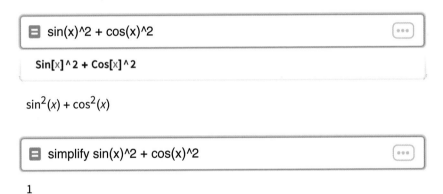

$$\sin^2(x) + \cos^2(x)$$

simplify sin(x)^2 + cos(x)^2

1

The software has built-in knowledge of many trigonometric identities, which can be applied to various expressions involving trigonometric functions.

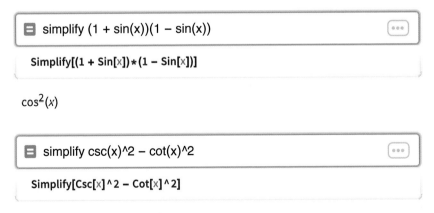

$$\cos^2(x)$$

simplify csc(x)^2 − cot(x)^2

1

# Trigonometry Graphics

The term "graph" can be used to create a graph involving trigonometric functions in a similar style to graphing any other equation. An optional second phrase can be used to specify a domain of 0 to $2\pi$ for the graph. The $\pi$ symbol is available in the **Special Characters** menu.

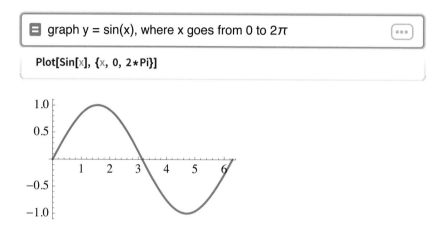

The upper and lower bounds for the $y$ axis can be specified in a calculation as well, and this is outlined later in the chapter.

The phrasing for creating graphs is flexible, and it is not necessary to include the "y =" phrase to create a graph of a trigonometric function.

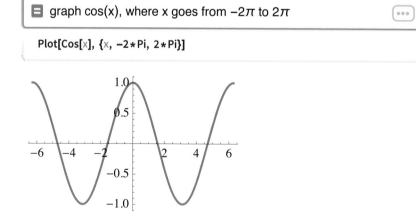

Graphs containing multiple trigonometric functions can be created by listing out the functions, separated by the term "and."

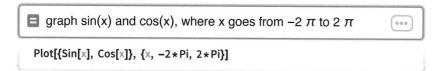

graph sin(x) and cos(x), where x goes from −2 π to 2 π

Plot[{Sin[x], Cos[x]}, {x, −2*Pi, 2*Pi}]

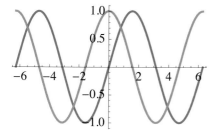

By default, Wolfram|Alpha Notebook Edition colors the two equations differently so the graph is easier to visually inspect.

Alternatively, functions can be listed in a calculation with parentheses and a comma, which is a useful notation when graphing three functions on one set of axes.

graph (sin(x), cos(x), tan(x)), where x goes from −4π to 4π

related computations⌄        full Wolfram|Alpha results

Plot[{Sin[x], Cos[x], Tan[x]}, {x, −4*Pi, 4*Pi}]

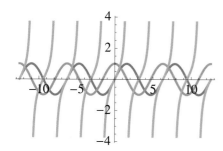

graph (sin (x), cos (x), tan (x)), where x goes from −4π to 4 π with legend

related computations⌄    full Wolfram|Alpha results

Plot[{Sin[x], Cos[x], Tan[x]}, {x, −4∗Pi, 4∗Pi}, PlotLegends −> True]

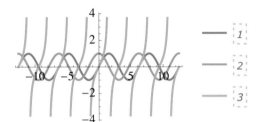

The Wolfram Language is needed to really have full customization of calculations and graphics (i.e. Mathematica). However, in Wolfram|Alpha Notebook Edition, it is possible to take some guesses with the Wolfram Language input to add additional customization. The best way to experiment is by copying and pasting Wolfram Language code into a new input cell, then typing directly into the code to edit. To evaluate the calculation, hold down the Shift key and press the Enter key at the same time. For example, see below on how to add specific text to the plot legend to associate the correct graphic with its function.

Plot[{Sin[x], Cos[x], Tan[x]}, {x, −4∗Pi, 4∗Pi}, PlotLegends −> {"sin(x), cos(x), tan(x)"}]

Plot[{Sin[x], Cos[x], Tan[x]}, {x, −4∗Pi, 4∗Pi}, PlotLegends −> {"sin(x), cos(x), tan(x)"}]

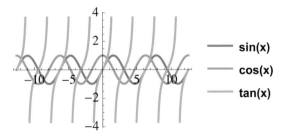

Visualizing trends when varying coefficients in trigonometric functions is an important part of many trigonometry courses or projects involving trig functions. The following calculation adds the symbol *a* to represent amplitude, and varies the symbol *a* from 1 to 4. By dragging the slider in the resulting mouse-driven model, the overall concept of amplitude can be visualized in real time much more efficiently compared to creating many graphs with many individual values.

graph a sin(x), x going from −2π to 2π, y going from −4 to 4, varying a from 1 to 4

full Wolfram|Alpha results

Manipulate[Plot[a*Sin[x], {x, −2*Pi, 2*Pi}, PlotRange -> {−4, 4}],
{{a, 5/2}, 1, 4, Appearance -> "Labeled"}]

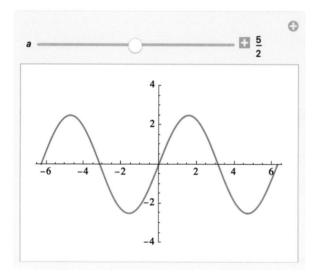

Varying a coefficient representing frequency is another common concept in trigonometry, and the following mouse-driven model varies the symbol $f$ from 1 to 4 to show the effects of increasing frequency on the graph in real time.

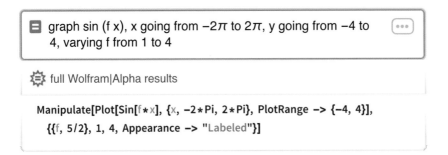

graph sin (f x), x going from −2π to 2π, y going from −4 to 4, varying f from 1 to 4

full Wolfram|Alpha results

Manipulate[Plot[Sin[f∗x], {x, −2∗Pi, 2∗Pi}, PlotRange −> {−4, 4}],
{{f, 5/2}, 1, 4, Appearance −> "Labeled"}]

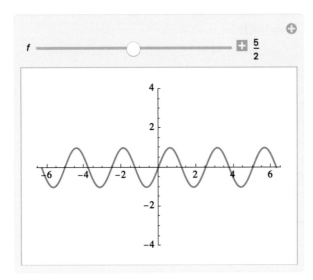

Any letter or special character can be used in a mouse-driven model. Using $f$ to represent frequency might be intuitive, but it is also possible to use any other letter or special character instead of $f$.

Phase shift can be explored with a similar calculation where the symbol $p$ is varied from -π to π.

graph sin(x + p), x going from −2π to 2π, y going from −4 to 4, varying p from −π to π

Manipulate[Plot[Sin[x + p], {x, −2∗Pi, 2∗Pi}, PlotRange −> {−4, 4}],
{{p, 0}, −Pi, Pi, Appearance −> "Labeled"}]

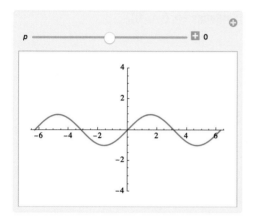

Horizontal shift is also another commonly discussed concept related to trigonometric functions, and the following input varies the symbol $h$ from $-\pi$ to $\pi$ to show effects on the graph in real time.

graph sin(x) + h, x going from −2π to 2π, y going from −4 to 4, varying h from −π to π

Manipulate[Plot[Sin[x] + h, {x, −2∗Pi, 2∗Pi}, PlotRange −> {−4, 4}],
{{h, 0}, −Pi, Pi, Appearance −> "Labeled"}]

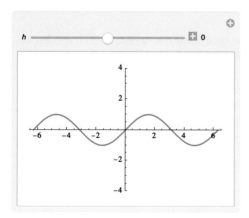

While the above examples all use the sine function, the same overall phrasing can be used to explore similar concepts for other trigonometric functions. The following calculation explores amplitude for a tangent function instead of a sine function.

> ▤ graph a tan(x), x going from −2π to 2π, y going from −4 to 4, varying a from 1 to 4    ⌜•••⌝

Manipulate[Plot[a∗Tan[x], {x, −2∗Pi, 2∗Pi}, PlotRange -> {−4, 4}],
{{a, 5/2}, 1, 4, Appearance -> "Labeled"}]

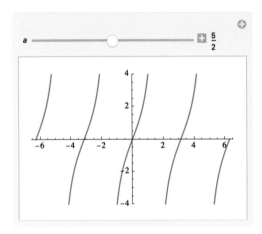

This chapter shows several commonly created mouse-driven models, but in a course setting, it is common to include more explanation or prompts for students to describe the patterns they see in their own words. The various text cells outlined in previous chapters are very useful in conjunction with mouse-driven models.

"Secant," "cosecant" and "cotangent" can also be used in similar mouse-driven models to explore variations when changing certain coefficients and the effects on the graph.

graph sec(x + p), x going from −2π to 2π, y going from −4 to 4, varying p from −π to π

full Wolfram|Alpha results

Manipulate[Plot[Sec[x + p], {x, −2*Pi, 2*Pi}, PlotRange −> {−4, 4}],
{{p, 0}, −Pi, Pi, Appearance −> "Labeled"}]

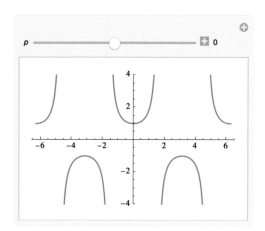

graph csc(x) + h, x going from −2π to 2π, y going from −4 to 4, varying h from −π to π

Manipulate[Plot[Csc[x] + h, {x, −2*Pi, 2*Pi}, PlotRange −> {−4, 4}],
{{h, 0}, −Pi, Pi, Appearance −> "Labeled"}]

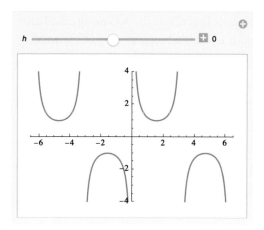

The inverse sine function can be entered into calculations using the standard notation, and inverse sine can be used either to calculate specific values or in a graph to compare inverse sine to the sine function.

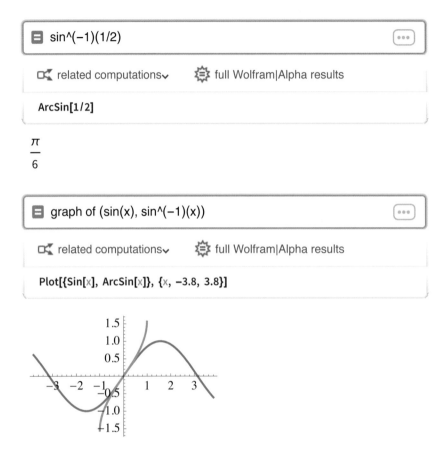

sin^(−1)(1/2)

related computations⌄    full Wolfram|Alpha results

ArcSin[1/2]

$$\frac{\pi}{6}$$

graph of (sin(x), sin^(−1)(x))

related computations⌄    full Wolfram|Alpha results

Plot[{Sin[x], ArcSin[x]}, {x, −3.8, 3.8}]

Previous chapters outlined solving equations in detail, and the same term "solve" can be used to solve equations that contain trigonometric functions. The following calculation also specifies a range for $x$, and a list of solutions is returned separated by OR symbols.

solve 2 sin(x)^2 + sin(x) = 0, 0 <= x < 2π

full Wolfram|Alpha results

Reduce[{2 ∗ Sin[x]^2 + Sin[x] == 0,
    Inequality[0, LessEqual, x, Less, 2 ∗ Pi]}, x]

$$x = 0 \lor x = \pi \lor x = \frac{7\pi}{6} \lor x = \frac{11\pi}{6}$$

## Elementary Functions

The term "set" can be used to define functions in calculations. This definition is retained either until the user clears the definition or until Wolfram|Alpha Notebook Edition is closed and restarted to start a new session.

Defining a function produces no result, but the function can be used to calculate the result based on a specific value. In this case, calculating $f(3)$ produces a result of 10.

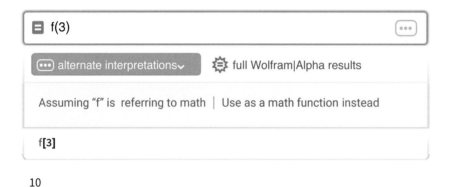

A calculation can include a user-defined function along with a larger calculation with multiple steps.

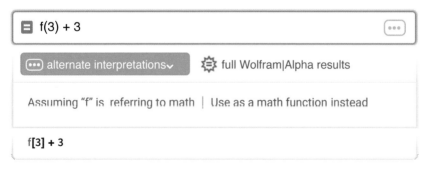

The original function is defined using a pattern and the symbol $x$. Using the symbol $t$ as an input for the function returns the function in terms of $t$ rather than $x$.

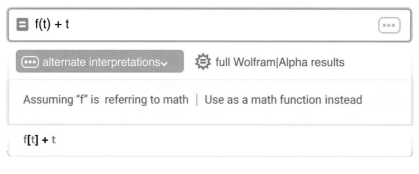

$4t + 1$

The same "set" term can be used to define a second function, the value of which will also be stored in the software until the function is cleared or until the software application is restarted.

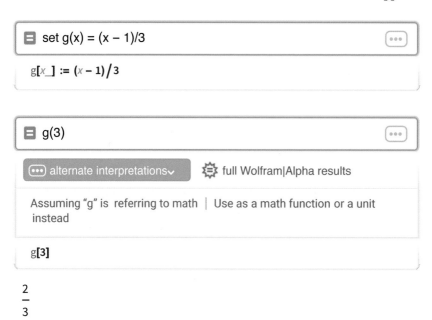

$$\frac{2}{3}$$

The term "clear" can be used to undefine a function and will be shown later in this chapter.

Wolfram|Alpha Notebook Edition contains a sophisticated set of solvers for precalculus and calculus. A calculation can involve nested functions where the function $g$ is being applied first to the specific value of $4$, then the function $f$ is being applied to that result. The two functions are inverse functions, so the result is the same as the input.

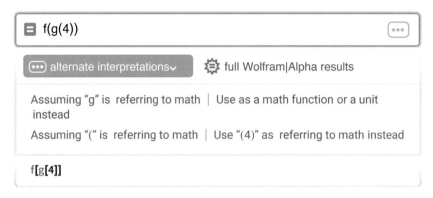

4

Instead of using specific values, use of the symbol $x$ also confirms the two functions are inverse functions.

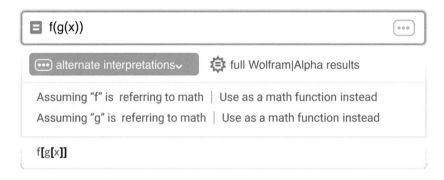

x

The two functions can be used in a compound input where a specific value is given to each function, and the result of $g(3)$ is subtracted from the result of $f(3)$.

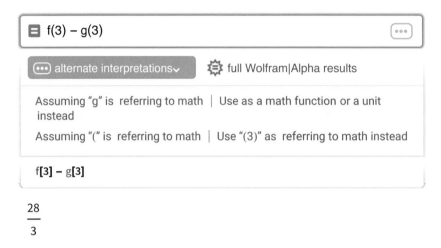

$$\frac{28}{3}$$

Functions can use a wide variety of variable names; it is not necessary to use the symbol $x$ to define the pattern for a function. The following function uses the symbol $t$ to define the pattern for the function.

 Function names can be words as well, in addition to single characters.

Functions $f$ and $h$ can be nested in a calculation since they are defining a pattern, and calculate results as expected. The functions use $x$ and $t$ to specify respective patterns, but will calculate results as expected when nesting the two functions. The function $h$ is applied to $-1$ first, then $f$ is applied to that result.

19

The term "clear" can be used to remove a function definition. The following calculation clears both $f(x)$ and $g(3)$ in the same input cell.

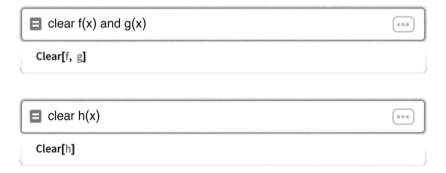

After evaluating the above calculations, the functions $f$, $g$ and $h$ have no stored values, and when they are used in a subsequent calculation, the result returns the function unevaluated.

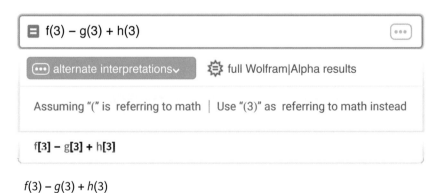

$f(3) - g(3) + h(3)$

Function definitions are specific to the order of when calculations are evaluated, not the order of calculations on the page. If the function *f* is undefined later in a notebook, and a previous calculation using *f* is reevaluated, that result will also not remember the definition of *f*.

## Conic Sections

Graphics in Wolfram|Alpha Notebook Edition are very flexible and can be used to visualize a number of concepts in advanced algebra or precalculus. Use of the term "graph" creates a graph of an ellipse in the following calculation.

graph of (x^2/64) + (y^2/39) = 1

ContourPlot[x ^2/64 + y ^2/39 == 1, {x, −10, 10}, {y, −7.8, 7.8}]

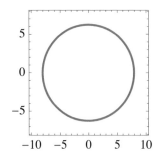

The following calculation creates a graph of a hyperbola.

graph of (y^2/49) − (x^2/32) = 1

ContourPlot[y ^2/49 − x ^2/32 == 1, {x, −33 − 4∗Sqrt[2], 33 + 4∗Sqrt[2]}, {y, −50, 50}]

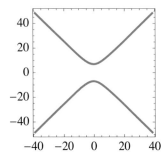

For implicit curves, the axes are drawn on the border instead of through the origin. The graph above is still centered around (0, 0).

The following calculation creates the graph of a parabola, and uses an option phrase to specify a domain for the plot going from −5 to 5.

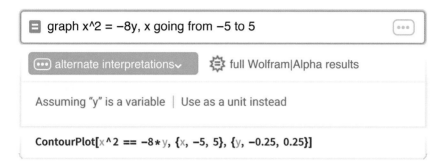

graph x^2 = −8y, x going from −5 to 5

alternate interpretations⌄    ⚙ full Wolfram|Alpha results

Assuming "y" is a variable  |  Use as a unit instead

ContourPlot[x^2 == −8*y, {x, −5, 5}, {y, −0.25, 0.25}]

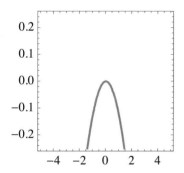

 While many of the calculations in this book do not specify upper and lower bounds for the $y$ axis on a graph, any calculation can specify a range for both the $x$ and $y$ axes. However, it is convenient that Wolfram|Alpha Notebook Edition chooses useful values automatically without specifying anything.

In general, calculations in Wolfram|Alpha Notebook Edition return a single result. This style is useful for creating a series of calculations, and provides clarity to the software when using terms like "that" or "result" to reference the results of a previous calculation.

For some calculations, however, the full Wolfram|Alpha results contain applications that can be more useful than the single results in the software. For a calculation related to surface of revolution, the result for a calculation to rotate an equation around a certain axis returns an equation of a parametric region. The full Wolfram|Alpha results, however, provide a nice mouse-driven model to visualize this concept.

rotate y = 2x, 0 < x < 3 around the y−axis

$$\text{ParametricRegion}[\{x*\text{Cos}[\theta],\ 2*x,\ x*\text{Sin}[\theta]\},\ \{\{x,\ 0,\ 3\},\ \{\theta,\ 0,\ 2*\text{Pi}\}\}]$$

$$\text{ParametricRegion}[\{\{x\cos(\theta),\ 2\,x,\ x\sin(\theta)\},\ 0\le x\le 3\wedge 0\le\theta\le 2\,\pi\},\ \{x,\ \theta\}]$$

## ✳ rotate y = 2x, 0 < x < 3 around the y-axis

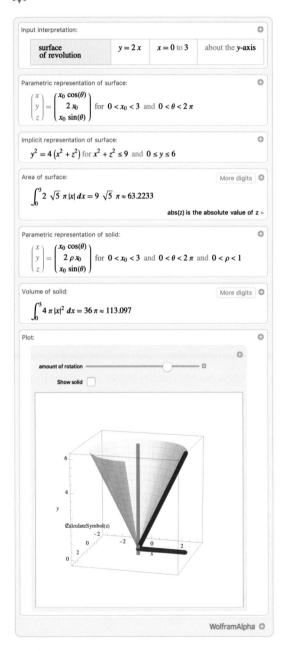

Input interpretation:

| surface of revolution | $y = 2\,x$ | $x = 0$ to $3$ | about the **y-axis** |
|---|---|---|---|

Parametric representation of surface:

$$\begin{pmatrix} x \\ y \\ z \end{pmatrix} = \begin{pmatrix} x_0\cos(\theta) \\ 2\,x_0 \\ x_0\sin(\theta) \end{pmatrix} \text{ for } 0 < x_0 < 3 \text{ and } 0 < \theta < 2\,\pi$$

Implicit representation of surface:

$$y^2 = 4\left(x^2 + z^2\right) \text{ for } x^2 + z^2 \le 9 \text{ and } 0 \le y \le 6$$

Area of surface: More digits

$$\int_0^3 2\,\sqrt{5}\,\pi\,|x|\,dx = 9\,\sqrt{5}\,\pi \approx 63.2233$$

abs(z) is the absolute value of z »

Parametric representation of solid:

$$\begin{pmatrix} x \\ y \\ z \end{pmatrix} = \begin{pmatrix} x_0\cos(\theta) \\ 2\,\rho\,x_0 \\ x_0\sin(\theta) \end{pmatrix} \text{ for } 0 < x_0 < 3 \text{ and } 0 < \theta < 2\,\pi \text{ and } 0 < \rho < 1$$

Volume of solid: More digits

$$\int_0^3 4\,\pi\,|x|^2\,dx = 36\,\pi \approx 113.097$$

Plot:

amount of rotation

Show solid

WolframAlpha

Users of the Wolfram|Alpha website might have favorite examples and an intuition for when to click the **full Wolfram|Alpha results** button. Those same favorite pods will be included in the series of results in Wolfram|Alpha Notebook Edition.

Graphs can also be based on polar coordinates by using the phrase "polar graph" prior to the equation. The $\theta$ symbol can be entered using the **Special Characters** menu.

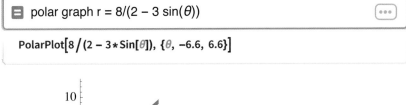

polar graph r = 8/(2 − 3 sin($\theta$))

PolarPlot$\left[8/(2 - 3 * \text{Sin}[\theta]), \{\theta, -6.6, 6.6\}\right]$

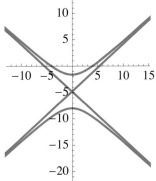

Polar graphs can include a cosine function instead of a sine function.

polar graph r = 2 + 3 cos($\theta$)

full Wolfram|Alpha results

PolarPlot$[2 + 3 * \text{Cos}[\theta], \{\theta, -6.6, 6.6\}]$

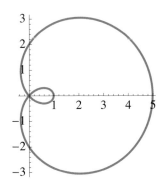

The term "varying" can also be used in polar graphs to visualize effects on the graph as the symbol $b$ varies from 3 to 5.

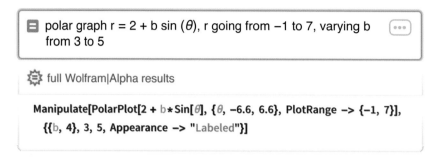

Manipulate[PolarPlot[2 + b*Sin[θ], {θ, −6.6, 6.6}, PlotRange −> {−1, 7}],
{{b, 4}, 3, 5, Appearance −> "Labeled"}]

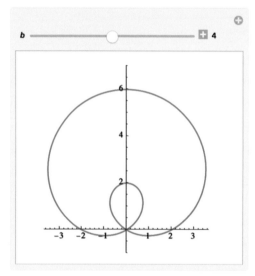

## Basics of Matrices

A matrix can be represented with nested parentheses, and in the following calculation, a 2×2 matrix is being multiplied by 2 to produce a result that is also in the form of a square matrix.

▤ 2 * ((1,2), (3,4))

📝 step-by-step solution    ⚙ full Wolfram|Alpha results

2*{{1, 2}, {3, 4}}

$$\begin{pmatrix} 2 & 4 \\ 6 & 8 \end{pmatrix}$$

The term "set" can be used to assign a value to a variable, and the value can be a matrix instead of a number.

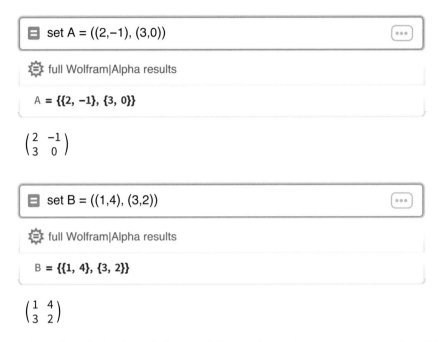

After values for both symbols $A$ and $B$ are defined, the two matrices can be added together.

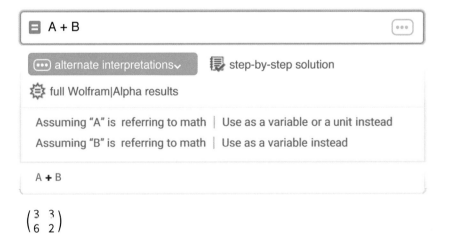

 Most variables or function names have been lowercase in this book, but using capital letters, which is more common for a matrix, is also supported.

Use of a period represents a dot product, and the following calculation returns the dot product for $A$ and $B$.

$$\begin{pmatrix} -1 & 6 \\ 3 & 12 \end{pmatrix}$$

The asterisk character is used to multiply two matrices together.

$$\begin{pmatrix} -1 & 6 \\ 3 & 12 \end{pmatrix}$$

The term "determinant" can be used to calculate the determinant of the matrix $A$.

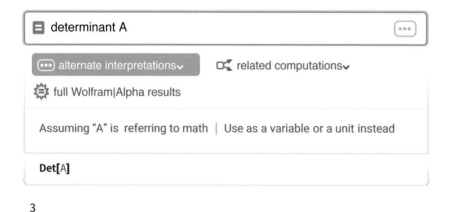

3

The values for $A$ and $B$ can be cleared such that these symbols can be used in subsequent calculations without any stored value.

> ▤ clear A, B     ⋯

⚙ full Wolfram|Alpha results

Clear[A, B]

# Sequences and Probability

The term "table" can be used in calculations to produce a result in the form of a list. These types of calculations create a table of values that is useful for defining and visualizing the progression of a sequence. The following calculation can be used to return the 10th value in the sequence 1, 3, 5, 7, 9 ....

> ▤ table (2a − 1), a = 1 to 10     ⋯

Table[2 * a − 1, {a, 1, 10}]

{1, 3, 5, 7, 9, 11, 13, 15, 17, 19}

> ✳ The result uses curly brackets to represent a list of values, and that is the convention for any list of results.

The sequence can have a more intricate set of calculations for each value; the following table of values involves a radical and multiple instances of the symbol $a$ within the sequence.

> ▤ table (2a^2 + a + 1), a = 1 to 10     ⋯

Table[2 * a ^ 2 + a + 1, {a, 1, 10}]

{4, 11, 22, 37, 56, 79, 106, 137, 172, 211}

When an undefined symbol is used in a sequence, the calculation returns a result in terms of that symbol. For example, the following sequence is returned in terms of the symbol $n$.

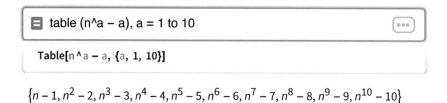

$$\{n-1, n^2-2, n^3-3, n^4-4, n^5-5, n^6-6, n^7-7, n^8-8, n^9-9, n^{10}-10\}$$

Testing an inequality can be incorporated in a table of values. The following example tests whether $3x+1$ is greater than 20 where $x$ starts at 1 and goes to 10 in steps of one. The result demonstrates that when $x = 7$, the result of $3(7)+1$ is greater than 20, and each larger value of $x$ is also greater than 20.

▤ table (3x + 1 > 20), x = 1 to 10　···

  Table[3*x + 1 > 20, {x, 1, 10}]

{False, False, False, False, False, False, True, True, True, True}

The **Special Characters** menu can be used to enter a summation sign. The following calculation sums the expression $2a-1$ as $a$ goes from 1 to 10 in steps of 1.

▤ Σ(2a – 1), a = 1 to 10　···

  Sum[2*a − 1, {a, 1, 10}]

100

The **Special Characters** menu can also be used to enter a product sign and multiply the expression $2a-1$ as $a$ goes from 1 to 10.

  Product[2*a − 1, {a, 1, 10}]

654 729 075

In addition to exploring sequences or trying many ideas to find a desired sequence, Wolfram|Alpha Notebook Edition includes knowledge of probabilities and how to apply probabilities to real-world scenarios. The following calculation creates a graph showing the probability of rolling any particular number on a six-sided die when the die is rolled once.

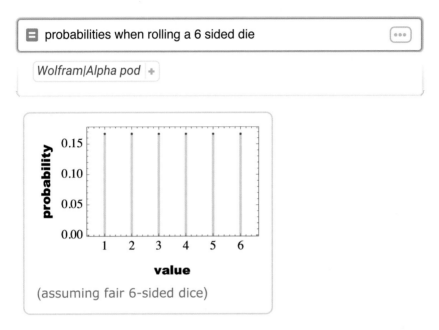

The probabilities are less uniform when rolling two dice. The following chart shows the probability of rolling a 3 when rolling two six-sided dice.

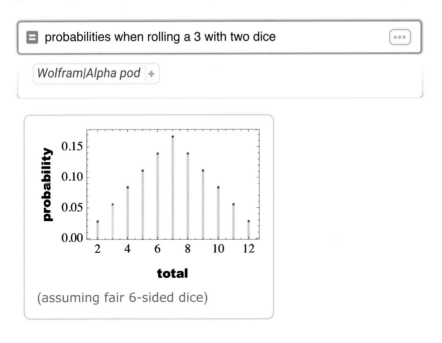

Clicking the **full Wolfram|Alpha results** button displays the series of results for this particular calculation, including some extra calculations that can be useful to related probabilities. In this case, the multiple outputs provide a numerical representation of the probability as well as the most likely outcome.

**probabilities when rolling a 3 with two dice**

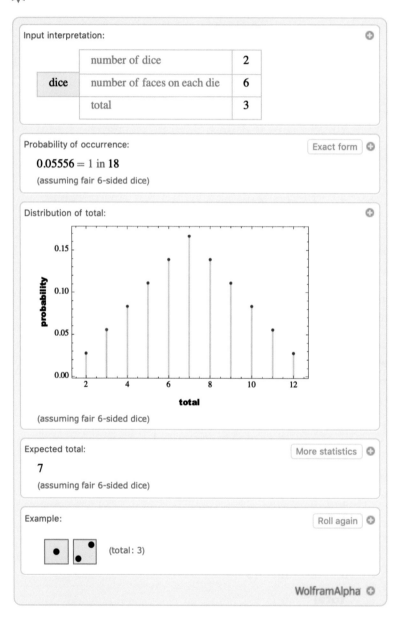

Input interpretation:

| dice | number of dice | 2 |
| --- | --- | --- |
| | number of faces on each die | 6 |
| | total | 3 |

Probability of occurrence:    Exact form

0.05556 = 1 in 18

(assuming fair 6-sided dice)

Distribution of total:

(assuming fair 6-sided dice)

Expected total:    More statistics

7

(assuming fair 6-sided dice)

Example:    Roll again

(total: 3)

WolframAlpha

Calculations related to probability might involve dates or a concept like a birthday. In the following calculation, Wolfram|Alpha Notebook Edition applies built-in knowledge about birthdays to calculate a probability.

> ▣ odds of 23 people having the same birthday ⋯
>
> 1 / 365 ^ (23 – 1)

1/234 662 135 214 110 469 141 956 898 203 822 336 135 218 143 463 134 765 625

> ▣ approximate that ⋯
>
> N[%]

$4.26145 \times 10^{-57}$

## Conclusion

Notebooks can support a wide variety of calculations and include supporting textual explanations of concepts, which is useful in trigonometry and precalculus to outline ideas through a wide variety of graphics or calculations using user-defined functions. Mouse-driven models are useful in many areas, but are especially useful in trigonometry to easily visualize variations and understand overall concepts.

## Exercises

1. Solve the inequality $\left| x - 5 \right| < x2 + 3$.

2. Solve the inequality $x\^3 - 7\,x\^2 + 6\,x < 0$.

3. Simplify the following expression: $(x\^3 - 27) / (x\^2 - 9)$.

4. Find the vertex of the parabola $f(x) = x2 - 4\,x + 4$.

5. Find the solution of the following equation: $x + 1 = \sqrt{(x + 7)}$.

6. Find the solutions of the following equation: $2 \times \sqrt[3]{2}\,x = x$.

7. Simplify $(\log(27) * \log(2)) / (\log(3) * \log(8))$.

8. Find the solutions of the equation $\ln(x) + \ln(x - 2) = \ln(2\,x - 3)$.

9. Simplify $\sin\left( \frac{7\pi}{6} \right)$.

10. Simplify $\cos\left( \frac{3\pi}{2} + x \right)$.

# Calculus in Wolfram|Alpha Notebook Edition

## Introduction

Wolfram|Alpha Notebook Edition is a nice environment to explore variations in calculations, and calculus is an area where seeing many variations and visualizations is especially useful for understanding concepts. Solving problems manually can also become a more time-consuming process, and the included step-by-step solutions can provide real-time insights for the mechanics of basically any problem in precollege or college calculus. This chapter will show several possible calculations to act as a guide for solving problems in calculus and visualizing concepts graphically.

## Differentiation

The term "differentiate" can be used to calculate a partial derivative with one or more variables. The phrase "with respect to x" is used to specify the variable of interest for the calculation.

$$x^2 \cos(x) + 2x \sin(x)$$

When a derivative involves only one variable, the phrase "with respect to x" can be removed, and the calculation still returns the desired result. This is one of many examples where the automation built into Wolfram|Alpha Notebook Edition provides flexibility to the user where the phrasing is concerned for a calculation. Each user can perform calculations with the phrasing that is most natural to them.

$$x^2 \cos(x) + 2x \sin(x)$$

The previous calculation used the variable $x$ as the variable of interest. However, if a calculation uses the variable $y$ instead, the calculation will automatically use that as the variable of interest. A calculation involving a derivative does not need to be entered using a common variable name like $x$.

$$y^2 \cos(y) + 2y \sin(y)$$

The same overall idea holds true if a variable name of $a$ is used instead of either $x$ or $y$.

$$a^2 \cos(a) + 2a \sin(a)$$

Several previous chapters outlined step-by-step solutions and how this can be used to check the mechanics of solving a particular problem. In calculus, the step-by-step solutions are more sophisticated and can outline typical steps to solve a wide variety of precollege- or college-level calculus problems. Clicking the **step-by-step solution** button in the previous calculation creates a new pairing of input and output cells for the step-by-step solution.

The solution for this particular problem involves the chain rule, which is outlined in one of the major steps to the solution. The user does not necessarily need to recognize the chain rule is the best approach for this particular problem; the software automatically recognizes common approaches outlined in textbooks to solve various problems, and the solutions can act as a real-time tutor to support homework sets or problems from a textbook.

show steps d/da(a^2 sin(a))

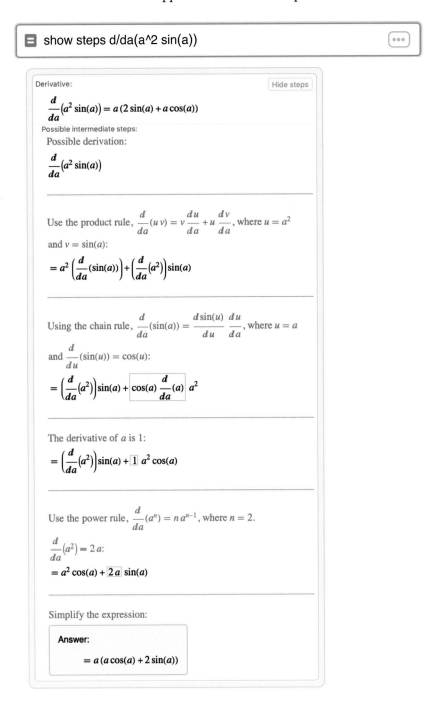

Derivative:

Hide steps

$$\frac{d}{da}(a^2 \sin(a)) = a\,(2\sin(a) + a\cos(a))$$

Possible intermediate steps:

Possible derivation:

$$\frac{d}{da}(a^2 \sin(a))$$

Use the product rule, $\frac{d}{da}(u\,v) = v\,\frac{du}{da} + u\,\frac{dv}{da}$, where $u = a^2$

and $v = \sin(a)$:

$$= a^2\left(\frac{d}{da}(\sin(a))\right) + \left(\frac{d}{da}(a^2)\right)\sin(a)$$

Using the chain rule, $\frac{d}{da}(\sin(a)) = \frac{d\sin(u)}{du}\,\frac{du}{da}$, where $u = a$

and $\frac{d}{du}(\sin(u)) = \cos(u)$:

$$= \left(\frac{d}{da}(a^2)\right)\sin(a) + \boxed{\cos(a)\,\frac{d}{da}(a)}\;a^2$$

The derivative of $a$ is 1:

$$= \left(\frac{d}{da}(a^2)\right)\sin(a) + \boxed{1}\;a^2\cos(a)$$

Use the power rule, $\frac{d}{da}(a^n) = n\,a^{n-1}$, where $n = 2$.

$$\frac{d}{da}(a^2) = 2\,a:$$

$$= a^2\cos(a) + \boxed{2a}\,\sin(a)$$

Simplify the expression:

Answer:

$$= a\,(a\cos(a) + 2\sin(a))$$

> Just like any other step-by-step solution, the solution can be displayed one step at a time so the user can compare their overall approach to the software, or all steps can be shown at once so the user can compare a manually created solution to the software.

Calculations can also use prime notation to represent a derivative. Since **Sin** is a built-in function in the software, use of prime notation calculates the derivative of sin(*x*).

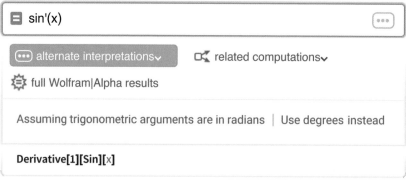

Cos[x]

Rather than using a built-in function like **Sin**, it is very common for a user to define functions related to calculus problems or visualizations. The term "set" can be used to define a function, and the following calculation defines $f(x)$ to a particular equation where *x* represents the pattern for the function definition.

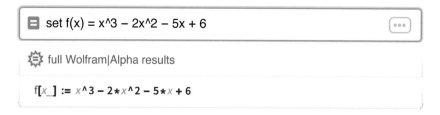

Once defined, calculating the result of $f(x)$ will simply return the expression in the function definition.

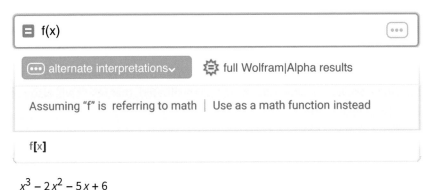

$$x^3 - 2x^2 - 5x + 6$$

When working with functions and defining functions in calculus, it is common to use names like $f(x)$ or $g(x)$ multiple times for multiple problems. A function definition can be reevaluated with a different equation and different variables, but for a longer notebook with many sets of definitions, it is often useful to clear a function. Clearing a function removes the stored value, and that symbol can be used in subsequent calculations for a different function definition.

The term "clear" can be used in a calculation to clear the value of the function $f$.

Reevaluating $f(x)$ confirms the function no longer has a specific definition.

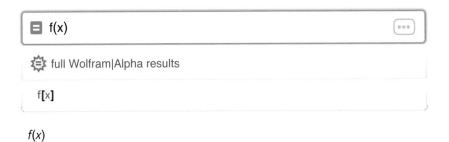

$f(x)$

Function definitions are specific to the order of when calculations are evaluated, not the order of calculations on the page. If the function *f* is undefined later in a notebook, and a previous calculation using *f* is reevaluated, that result will also not remember the definition of *f*.

The subsequent calculations in this chapter will use a slightly different definition for $f(x)$ compared to the previous definition earlier in the chapter. The following calculation defines $f(x)$ with a new pattern based on the variable $x$. Any previous calculations using the prior definition of $f(x)$ will remain intact as an archive for that series of calculations.

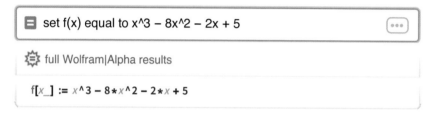

set f(x) equal to x^3 − 8x^2 − 2x + 5

❖ full Wolfram|Alpha results

$f[x\_] := x^3 - 8*x^2 - 2*x + 5$

Prime notation can be used with a user-defined function to calculate the derivative of $f(x)$. This style is similar to the use of prime notation earlier in the chapter to calculate the derivative of $\sin(x)$.

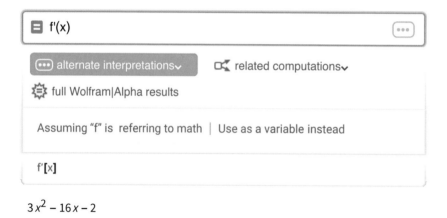

f'(x)

••• alternate interpretations⌄        related computations⌄

❖ full Wolfram|Alpha results

Assuming "f" is referring to math  |  Use as a variable instead

f'[x]

$3x^2 - 16x - 2$

The following calculation finds the value of *f* at 5.

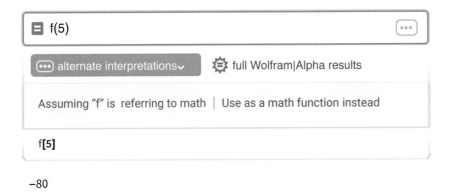

−80

The function *f* can be used more than once; the following calculation finds the value of *f* at 5, then finds the value of *f* at the result of *f* (5).

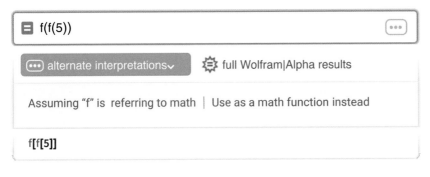

−563 035

In addition to calculating values of a function corresponding to specific numerical values, symbols can be inserted into the function as well. The following calculation finds the value of *f* at *a*, then the value of *f* at *f* (*a*).

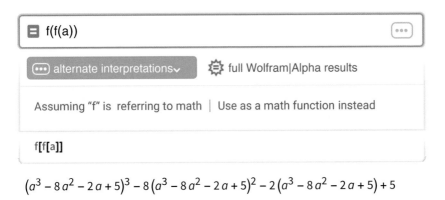

$$\left(a^3 - 8a^2 - 2a + 5\right)^3 - 8\left(a^3 - 8a^2 - 2a + 5\right)^2 - 2\left(a^3 - 8a^2 - 2a + 5\right) + 5$$

A user-defined function can also be used in a graph using the term "graph."

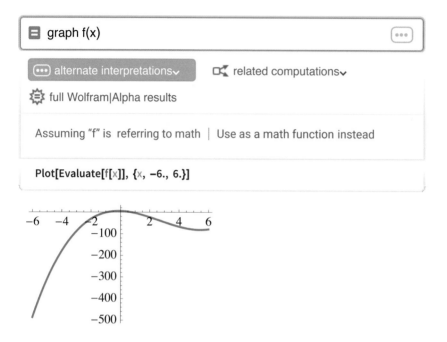

In many calculations in this book involving graphics, the calculation does not specify any upper or lower bounds for the *x* or *y* axes. Both can be specified in the calculation for a customized viewpoint.

In addition to visualizing the original function, a calculation can specify both a function and its derivative to create a graph of both on the same set of axes.

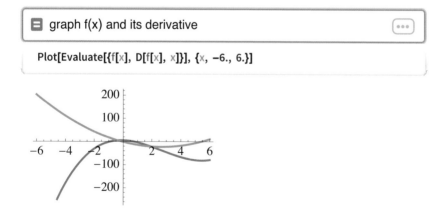

While the **Writing Assistant** palette, located in the **Palettes** drop-down menu, is primarily used to create symbols and typesetting in text cells, it also contains a palette called **Drawing Tools** to annotate graphics. After clicking the **Drawing Tools** button, a new palette is displayed to overlay text, geometric shapes and lines or arrows on an existing graphical result.

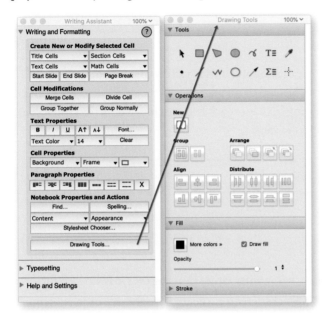

The following calculation creates the same graph of $f(x)$ and $f'(x)$, and uses the arrow button in the **Drawing Tools** palette to create lines with arrows, as well as the text button to create labels for $f(x)$ and $f'(x)$, which are overlaid on the graph.

graph f(x) and its derivative

Plot[Evaluate[{f[x], D[f[x], x]}], {x, −6., 6.}]

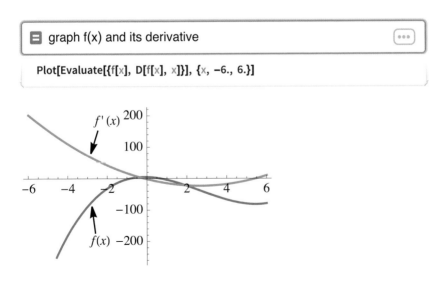

When the notebook is saved, the annotations created with the **Drawing Tools** palette are saved as well.

## Limits

Wolfram|Alpha Notebook Edition can also solve a wide variety of problems involving limits, and the phrase "limit for" can be used to calculate both straightforward limits and more intricate problems. The phrasing "as x approaches 1" specifies a direction and value where the limit approaches that specific value.

Limit[1/x, x -> 1]

1

A limit can be calculated as $x$ approaches infinity either by using everyday English for "infinity" or by using the **Special Character** menu at the upper-right side of the notebook and inserting a typeset character for infinity.

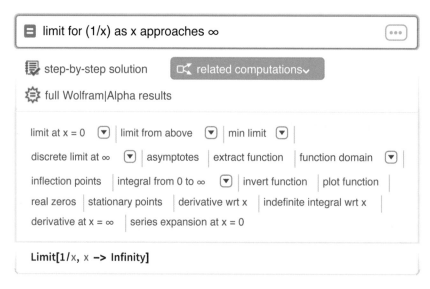

Limit[1/x, x -> Infinity]

0

The **related computations** button can be used to create a new pair of input and output cells to graph this function and compare the graph with the result of the limit in the previous calculation.

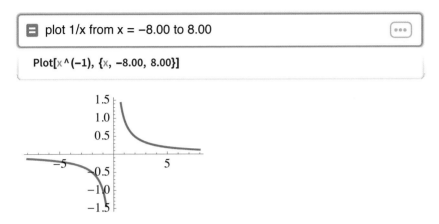

Many graphs in this chapter have been single visualizations, but for a concept like limits, it is sometimes useful to create several graphs for visual inspection. In the following graph, the *x* axis is extended to a much larger value to inspect corresponding values on the *y* axis. The phrasing for the previous calculation can be copied and pasted into a new input cell to quickly calculate an alternate view.

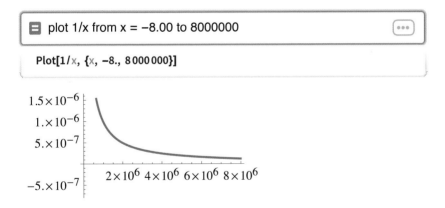

Directionality is also an important aspect of calculating limits, and in the following calculation, the directionality changes the result of the calculation. Use of the phrase "from the left" provides the desired directionality for the calculation.

```
limit for (1/x) as x approaches 0 from the left        ...
```

Limit[1/x, x -> 0, Direction -> 1]

$-\infty$

Changing the phrasing for directionality to "from the right" produces a result of ∞ instead of -∞.

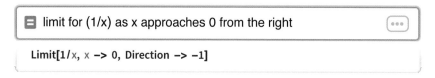

∞

---

 Results can include special characters like $\pi$ when displaying an exact result, and ∞ is also returned as a symbol when it is part of a result.

Since the result of the calculation is dependent on directionality in this case, if no directionality is specified in the calculation, the result will be **Indeterminate**.

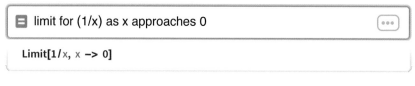

Indeterminate

A result of 0 is returned once the directionality is specified.

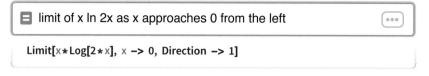

0

---

 Use of ln in the previous calculation represents a natural log.

For certain calculations, use of a general phrase in a calculation creates a separate set of input fields specific to the parameters for that particular calculation or visualization. The phrase "tangent line calculator" creates two input fields to enter a function as well as a point, and the result is a list of several equations representing that tangent line at that point along with a graphical representation of the function with the tangent line.

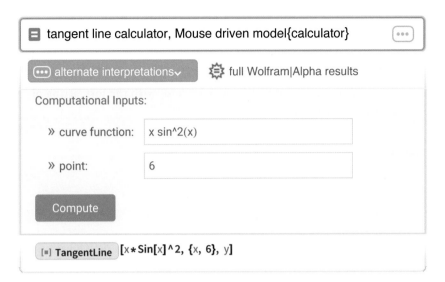

tangent line calculator, Mouse driven model{calculator}  ⋯

⋯ alternate interpretations⌄     ⚙ full Wolfram|Alpha results

Computational Inputs:

» curve function:   x sin^2(x)

» point:   6

Compute

[≡] **TangentLine**  $[x * \text{Sin}[x]\wedge 2, \{x, 6\}, y]$

⟨| SlopeInterceptEquation →

$$y = \left(12 \cos(6) \sin(6) + \sin^2(6)\right) x - 6\left(12 \cos(6) \sin(6) + \sin^2(6)\right) + 6 \sin^2(6),$$

PointSlopeEquation → $y - 6 \sin^2(6) = (x - 6)\left(12 \cos(6) \sin(6) + \sin^2(6)\right),$

StandardFormEquation → $y - x\left(12 \cos(6) \sin(6) + \sin^2(6)\right) =$

$\quad 6 \sin^2(6) - 6\left(12 \cos(6) \sin(6) + \sin^2(6)\right),$ Slope → $12 \cos(6) \sin(6) + \sin^2(6),$

VerticalIntercept → $6 \sin^2(6) - 6\left(12 \cos(6) \sin(6) + \sin^2(6)\right),$

HorizontalIntercept → $-\dfrac{6 \sin^2(6) - 6\left(12 \cos(6) \sin(6) + \sin^2(6)\right)}{12 \cos(6) \sin(6) + \sin^2(6)},$

Plot →

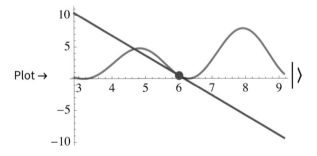

|⟩

This is also a case where clicking the **full Wolfram|Alpha results** button might be preferable for the sake of formatting. After clicking that button, a new pair of input and output cells is generated in which the information in the previous result is formatted more like the results on the Wolfram|Alpha website. When saving the notebook, the user might choose to retain just the WolframAlpha.com pods with the formatting of the website, or both sets of input cells.

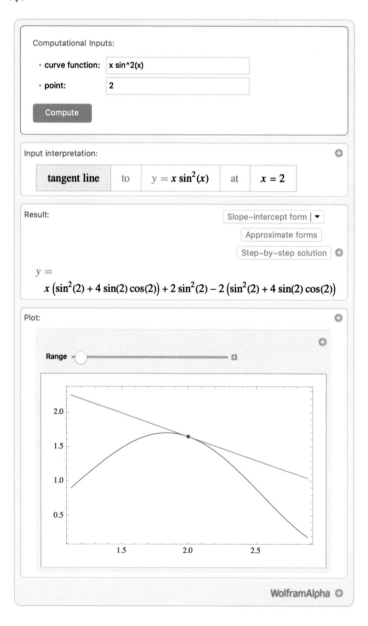

### tangent line calculator

Computational Inputs:

- curve function: `x sin^2(x)`
- point: `2`

Compute

Input interpretation:

| tangent line | to | $y = x \sin^2(x)$ | at | $x = 2$ |

Result:

Slope–intercept form | ▾

Approximate forms

Step-by-step solution ⊕

$$y = x \left(\sin^2(2) + 4 \sin(2) \cos(2)\right) + 2 \sin^2(2) - 2 \left(\sin^2(2) + 4 \sin(2) \cos(2)\right)$$

Plot:

WolframAlpha ⊕

# Integration

In the area of integration, the term "integrate" can be used to solve a wide variety of integrals, ranging from straightforward problems to very sophisticated integrals found in advanced courses or real-world projects. The following calculation calculates an integral for a particular function with respect to $x$.

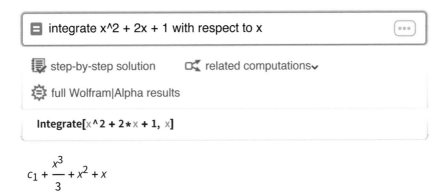

$$c_1 + \frac{x^3}{3} + x^2 + x$$

While the longer phrase "with respect to x" can be used to specify a variable of interest in an integral, the more conventional term of "dx" can also be used in a calculation of an integral.

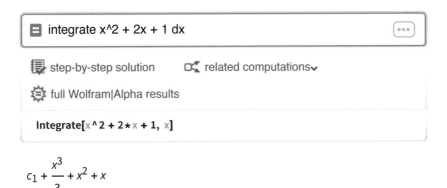

$$c_1 + \frac{x^3}{3} + x^2 + x$$

The default setting for results is to lead with the constant of integration, and at the time of the writing of this book, it is not possible to make that constant of integration the last term in the result.

In addition to the term "integrate," a calculation of an integral can also use typeset notation for an integral symbol to more closely mirror a typical textbook. The symbol for an indefinite integral can be found in the **Special Characters** menu.

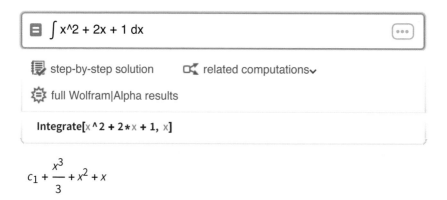

$$c_1 + \frac{x^3}{3} + x^2 + x$$

Calculations for integrals provide flexibility in phrasing that is similar to the flexibility in phrasing for derivatives. When calculating an integral with one variable, it is not necessary to include the phrase "with respect to x" or the term "dx" in the calculation.

> ▤ $\int$ x^2 + 2x + 1                                         ⋯
>
> **Integrate[**x^2 + 2*x + 1, x**]**

$$c_1 + \frac{x^3}{3} + x^2 + x$$

Any of the methods for solving integrals outlined in this chapter can be used to solve a wide variety of problems, including integrals involving trigonometric functions.

> ▤ $\int$ sin(x) + cos(x)                                       ⋯
>
> **Integrate[Sin[**x**] + Cos[**x**], x]**

$$c_1 + \sin(x) - \cos(x)$$

The software contains a powerful solver for integrals and can quickly solve more advanced problems as well.

∫ 1/(1 + x^3)

Integrate[1/(1 + x^3), x]

$$c_1 - \frac{1}{6} \log(x^2 - x + 1) + \frac{1}{3} \log(x + 1) + \frac{\tan^{-1}\left(\frac{2x-1}{\sqrt{3}}\right)}{\sqrt{3}}$$

To solve a definite integral, the phrase "from 0 to 1" can be used to specify the lower and upper bounds for the integral.

∫ x^2 + 2x + 1 from 0 to 1

Integrate[x^2 + 2*x + 1, {x, 0, 1}]

$$\frac{7}{3}$$

The **Writing Assistant** palette can only be used in text cells. So while it can create a symbol for a definite integral, that is meant for formulas in the text and cannot be used in calculations.

Instead of using numeric values for the lower and upper bounds of a definite integral, calculations can also use variables or symbols to return a more general result.

∫ x^2 + 2x + 1 from a to b

Integrate[x^2 + 2*x + 1, {x, a, b}]

$$-\frac{a^3}{3} + 2\left(\frac{b^2}{2} - \frac{a^2}{2}\right) - a + \frac{b^3}{3} + b$$

The typical convention of "ln(x)" can be used when calculating an integral of a function involving a natural log.

$$c_1 + \frac{3x^2}{2} - x + x\log(x)$$

Clicking the **step-by-step solution** button creates a new pair of input and output cells showing the mechanics for solving this integral. Integration by parts is used to solve the problem, so the software acts as a real-time tutor for problem sets and mirrors typical explanations from textbooks on how to solve this problem.

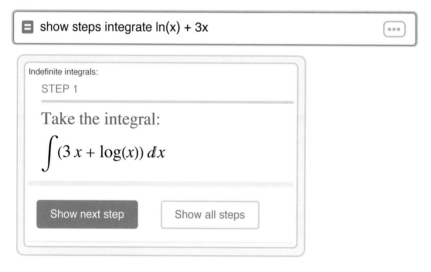

 For many of the step-by-step solutions in this chapter, only the first step of the solution will be displayed to save space. The reader should practice generating the step-by-step solution and viewing the steps in their own copy of the software.

For visualizations related to integration, it can be useful to plot specific functions and fill in the region between the axis and the curve. The phrase "with filling" can be added to the end of a calculation to create a graph to produce this filling effect.

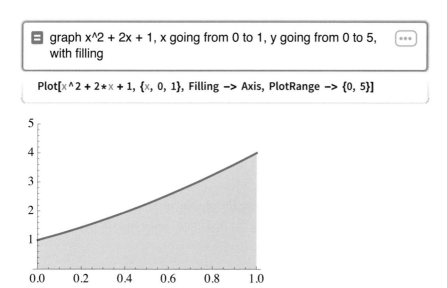

graph x^2 + 2x + 1, x going from 0 to 1, y going from 0 to 5, with filling

Plot[x^2 + 2*x + 1, {x, 0, 1}, Filling -> Axis, PlotRange -> {0, 5}]

In some cases, calculations can specify a general concept, and a set of input fields is created specific to this concept. For example, the phrase "area between two curves calculator" creates two input fields to enter two functions, and the calculation returns the area between the two curves.

area between two curves calculator

••• alternate interpretations∨    ⚙ full Wolfram|Alpha results

Computational Inputs:

» curve 1:   x^2+4x

» curve 2:   x

Compute

Also include: end points

[=] AreaBetweenCurves [{x^2 + 4*x, x}, x]

$$\frac{9}{2}$$

It is possible to enter different equations and recalculate the area between the curves, but when doing that, the new calculation will replace the previous one. So it is sometimes useful to have several calculations that each display these input fields to compare one result against another.

## Maxima and Minima

Calculations can identify a maximum value using the phrase "maximum value of" and can produce a result in the form of a list containing the maximum value and the corresponding point on the $x$ axis for that maximum value.

> ▤  maximum value of 1/(x^2 + 1)                                       •••
>
> Maximize$\left[1/(x{\wedge}2 + 1), \{x\}\right]$

$\{1, \{x \to 0\}\}$

It is often useful to visually inspect a function to confirm a maximum value, and the software automatically shows relevant regions in a function that are often related to maxima and minima.

> ▤  graph of 1/(x^2 + 1)                                              •••
>
> Plot$\left[1/(x{\wedge}2 + 1), \{x, -0.67, 0.67\}\right]$

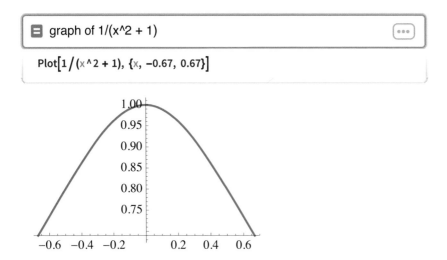

Similar phrasing can be used to calculate a minimum value, and a region can be specified with inequalities in a calculation as needed to find a minimum value within that specific region.

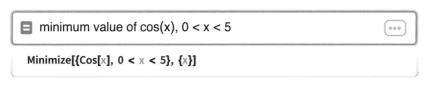

minimum value of cos(x), 0 < x < 5

Minimize[{Cos[x], 0 < x < 5}, {x}]

$\{-1, \{x \to \pi\}\}$

Similar visual inspection is useful to confirm this minimum value within a certain region.

 Just like other calculations, Wolfram|Alpha Notebook Edition returns an exact result of $\pi$ for the minimum value, not a decimal approximation.

graph cos x from 0 to 5

Plot[Cos[x], {x, 0, 5}]

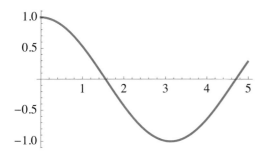

For lengthier equations, defining a function can be a useful first step when performing a series of calculations related to extrema.

set f(x) = x^3 − 3x^2 − 9x − 3

f[x_] := x^3 − 3*x^2 − 9*x − 3

Rather than finding minimum or maximum values separately, the phrase "find local extrema" provides both a local minimum and local maximum value in the same result.

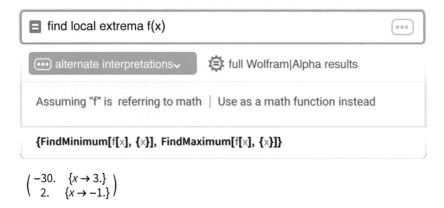

$$\begin{pmatrix} -30. & \{x \to 3.\} \\ 2. & \{x \to -1.\} \end{pmatrix}$$

The defined function can be used to create a graph with appropriate values for the $x$ axis to see the local extrema.

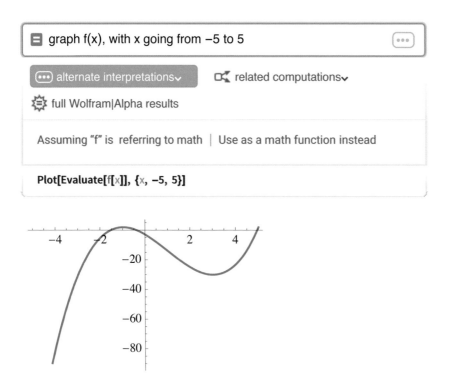

A single calculation can return a list of results related to the derivative of a function at specific points. The following calculation tests whether the derivative is positive or negative to provide further insight into whether $f$ is increasing or decreasing at these certain points.

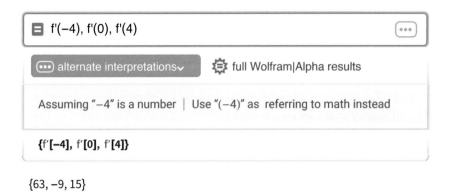

> ▤ f'(−4), f'(0), f'(4)    ⋯

> ⋯ alternate interpretations⌄    ⚙ full Wolfram|Alpha results

> Assuming "−4" is a number  |  Use "(−4)" as referring to math instead

> {f'[−4], f'[0], f'[4]}

{63, −9, 15}

---

These results are most useful when compared to the graph to confirm the results and gain a larger understanding of derivatives.

For certain calculations, a more general phrase can be used to create an application with input fields for a specific concept. In the case of Newton's method, three input fields are created to specify an equation, an initial point and a variable for the calculation.

> ▤ newton's method    ⋯

> ⋯ alternate interpretations⌄    ⚙ full Wolfram|Alpha results

> Assuming "newton's method" is a computation  |  Use as referring to a mathematical definition or a general topic instead

> Computational Inputs:

> » equation to solve:  −2 x + x^3

> » initial point:  2

> » variable:  x

> Compute

> Assuming equation to solve  |  Use root of a number instead

> FindRoot[−2∗x + x^3, {x, 2},
>    Method −> {"Newton", "StepControl" −> None}]

{x → 1.41421}

# Conclusion

In the area of calculus, Wolfram|Alpha Notebook Edition can solve a wide scope of problems, and can choose appropriate methods to solve problems automatically. This applies to calculations involving derivatives, limits or integrals to visualize variations in results or step-by-step solutions to confirm understanding of the mechanics of a solution. Since the same method is used for all step-by-step solutions, those solutions can act both as a real-time tutor for a specific problem and as a tutor for what approach to take to solve a problem.

# Exercises

1. Solve the following: limit of $(8 - 3x + 12x^2)$ as $x$ approaches 2.

2. Evaluate the given limit: $\lim \ln(4 - 9t - t^3)$ as $t$ approaches $-\infty$.

3. Differentiate the following: $\sin(w) + w^2 * \tan^{-1}(w)$.

4. Show the steps of the following differentiation: $\tan(4 + 10u)$.

5. Integrate $40x^3 + 12x^2 - 9x + 14$.

6. Use the integral symbol to integrate $(t^2 - 1)(4 + 3t)$.

7. Graph the result from Exercise 6.

8. Compute the following definite integral: $12x^3 - 9x^2 + 2$ from 1 to 6.

9. Compute the following definite integral: $3(4x + x^4)(10x^2 + x^5 - 2)^6$ from 0 to 1.

10. Approximate the result from Exercise 9 to eight digits.

# CHAPTER 15

# Statistics in Wolfram|Alpha Notebook Edition

## Introduction

In addition to working with functions and equations, Wolfram|Alpha Notebook Edition can perform many statistical tests on lists of numbers and generate many types of useful charts. The automation built into the software sometimes provides both charts and statistical tests in the same result for a calculation. The built-in knowledge of distributions and real-world data is also useful as a basis for introductory statistics problems. This chapter will outline several calculations and visualizations to act as a guide for exploring statistics concepts.

## Descriptive Statistics

A list of numbers can be used in a calculation by using parentheses as well as commas to separate each number in the list. Calculating a mean or average of a list of numbers can be performed with the term "mean of"; the result is returned in an exact form, which is the convention for any calculation in the software.

---

▤  mean of (2,3,3,4,5,4,3,5,2,3)                                  ⋯

---

📝 step-by-step solution        ⊄ related computations⌄

⚙ full Wolfram|Alpha results

Mean[{2, 3, 3, 4, 5, 4, 3, 5, 2, 3}]

---

$$\frac{17}{5}$$

Use of the term "result" references the result of the previous calculation. The following calculation approximates the mean of the list of numbers to three digits.

3.40

Several statistical tests are available in the software, including calculating the median value of a list.

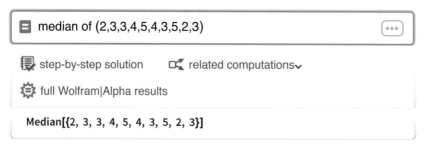

3

Calculating the mode of a list returns the value with the highest frequency in the list.

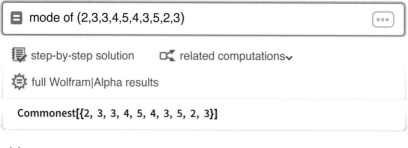

{3}

 The previous result indicates that 3 is the most common element in the list. It is displaying the value, not the frequency. The value of 3 occurs in the list four times.

For calculations on certain datasets, the existence of an outlier in the data might not be apparent when visually inspecting the list. The following calculation includes the value 54 in the middle of the list, which might be the result of a typing error.

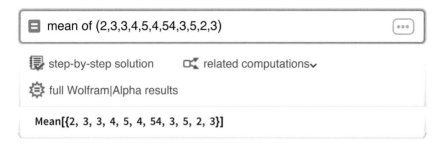

8

The term "max" can be used to calculate the maximum value in a list, which is a useful approach to identify potential outliers in a dataset.

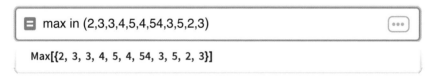

54

---

The terms "min" or "minimum" can also be used in calculations to find the smallest value in the list to spot outliers in a dataset.

The term "sort" can also be used to sort a list in ascending order. The result of the calculation provides a useful alternative for spotting an outlier that is either much larger or much smaller compared to the other values in the list.

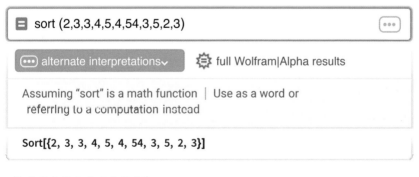

{2, 2, 3, 3, 3, 3, 4, 4, 5, 5, 54}

While it is useful to calculate specific statistical tests by name, entering a list of numbers can also be useful to view the full Wolfram|Alpha results and see many results all at once.

After clicking the **full Wolfram|Alpha results** button, a new pair of input and output cells is created with several suggestions for common statistical tests and charts for the dataset. The various calculations are listed in a collection of pods that mirrors the results on the Wolfram|Alpha website.

{2, 3, 3, 4, 5, 4, 3, 5, 2, 3}

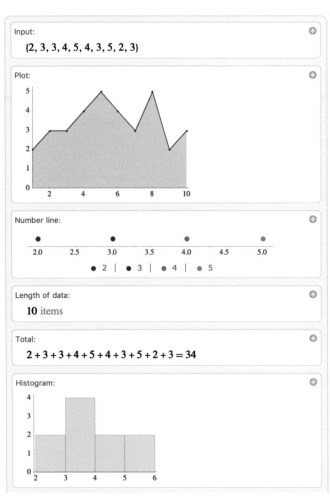

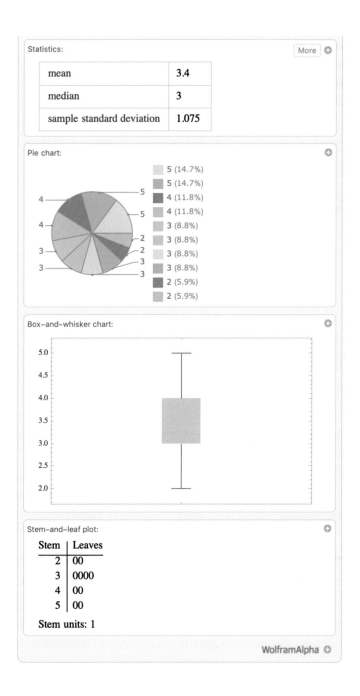

Statistics:    More ○

| mean | 3.4 |
| median | 3 |
| sample standard deviation | 1.075 |

Pie chart:

- 5 (14.7%)
- 5 (14.7%)
- 4 (11.8%)
- 4 (11.8%)
- 3 (8.8%)
- 3 (8.8%)
- 3 (8.8%)
- 3 (8.8%)
- 2 (5.9%)
- 2 (5.9%)

Box–and–whisker chart:

Stem–and–leaf plot:

| Stem | Leaves |
|---|---|
| 2 | 00 |
| 3 | 0000 |
| 4 | 00 |
| 5 | 00 |

Stem units: 1

WolframAlpha ○

The box-and-whisker chart provides statistical values when mousing over different parts of the chart. Creating specific charts will be outlined in more detail later in this chapter.

Similar to previous chapters and examples related to step-by-step solutions, the phrase "show steps" can be used in many statistical calculations to show the major steps of the solution. When using this phrase in a calculation involving standard deviation, the first step in this particular solution is to define a formula for variance, then subsequent steps apply that formula to the dataset to calculate standard deviation.

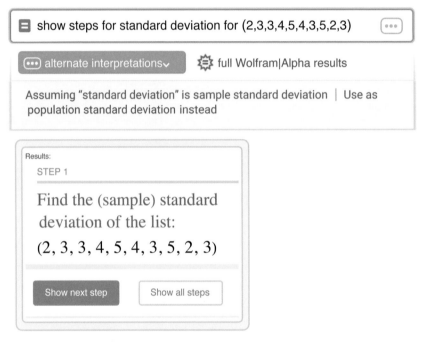

This step-by-step solution includes 11 major steps, which can be displayed one step at a time using the **Show next step** button, or all at once using the **Show all steps** button.

When a user wants to check their overall approach to a problem, the **Show next step** button is a convenient way to think through the major steps of a solution and acts as a real-time quiz for the user. The **Show all steps** button is often useful to check the software's step-by-step solution against a manually created solution.

Some statistical concepts involve a custom formula that is used with measured data to calculate a statistical measurement. In volleyball, the concept of hitting percentage is calculated through a total quantity of kills, errors and attempts in a specific span of time.

$$\text{hitting percentage} = \frac{(\text{kills} - \text{errors})}{\text{attemps}}$$

This formula can be used in a calculation, represented with single characters, where the specific athlete has 7 kills, 2 errors and 19 attempts.

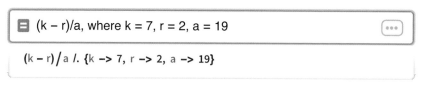

(k − r)/a /. {k -> 7, r -> 2, a -> 19}

$$\frac{5}{19}$$

 *e* is used to represent a specific concept of the exponential function, so the formula above uses "r" to represent errors, rather than "e."

This statistic is typically expressed as a percentage, so the exact decimal form in the previous result can be converted to a percentage in a separate calculation. The athlete has a hitting percentage of roughly 26%.

5/19 as a percentage

UnitConvert[0.2632, "Percent"]

26.32%

The concept of conversion rate in marketing can also be calculated with a custom formula involving measured data for the quantity of clicks on an advertisement versus the quantity of web store transactions.

$$\text{conversion rate} = \frac{\text{quantity of transactions in store}}{\text{quantity of clicks on an advertisement}}$$

This formula can be used to calculate the quantity of transactions that are necessary to achieve a 10% conversion rate if the advertisement had previously generated 11 transactions out of a total of 125 clicks on the ad, with an additional 200 clicks in the future. The term "solve" can be used to calculate the solution for the variable $t$, which represents the desired quantity of transactions for the next 200 clicks.

solve (11 + t)/(125 + 200) = 0.1, for t

$$\text{Solve}\left[(11 + t)/(125 + 200) == 0.1, t\right]$$

$$\{\{t \rightarrow 21.5\}\}$$

The term "ceiling" can be used to round a number up to the nearest integer, and the result can be applied to the conversion-rate formula to determine the exact conversion rate based on 22 transactions.

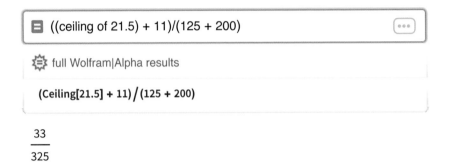

((ceiling of 21.5) + 11)/(125 + 200)

full Wolfram|Alpha results

$$(\text{Ceiling}[21.5] + 11) / (125 + 200)$$

$$\frac{33}{325}$$

 A transaction can only be an integer, so a solution involving half of a transaction should be rounded up to the nearest integer. Think of this like orders on a website: a customer places an order or does not place an order, but they cannot halfway place an order (although there are different concepts in marketing related to this).

Conversion rate is usually expressed as a percentage, so the exact solution in the previous result can be converted to a percentage. The resulting conversion rate is just above 10%.

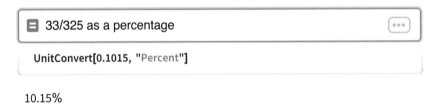

33/325 as a percentage

UnitConvert[0.1015, "Percent"]

10.15%

## Charts and Graphics

In a previous section, the **full Wolfram|Alpha results** button was used to generate a variety of charts for a particular dataset. Individual calculations can generate specific charts and graphics as well. The phrase "graph of" can be used with a dataset to create a graph of the points.

graph of (2,3,3,4,5,4,3,5,2,3)    •••

ListPlot[{2, 3, 3, 4, 5, 4, 3, 5, 2, 3}]

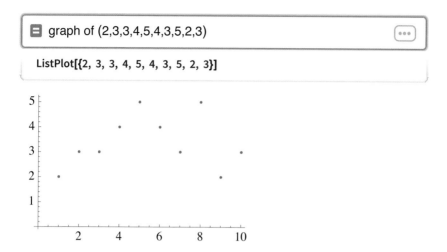

When exploring common values, a list can be sorted and then graphed in sorted form. This is a useful way to explore the concept of mode in visual form.

sort (2,3,3,4,5,4,3,5,2,3)    •••

••• alternate interpretations⌄    ⚙ full Wolfram|Alpha results

Assuming "sort" is a math function │ Use as a word or referring to a computation instead

Sort[{2, 3, 3, 4, 5, 4, 3, 5, 2, 3}]

{2, 2, 3, 3, 3, 3, 4, 4, 5, 5}

graph that    •••

ListPlot[{2, 2, 3, 3, 3, 3, 4, 4, 5, 5}]

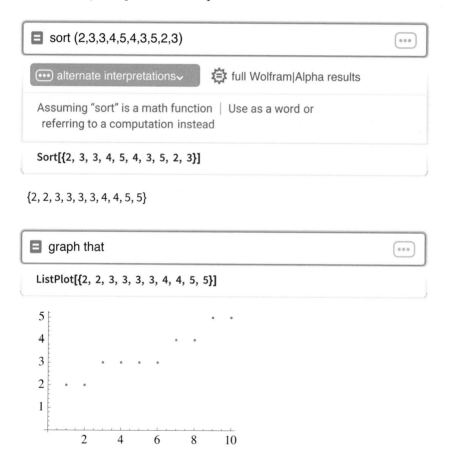

Sorting and then creating a graph might not be an ideal approach if the ordering of the data is important. For example, the ordering might represent a unit of time, which would make the ordering important.

A histogram is an alternate approach to visualize common values in a dataset. The following chart demonstrates the value 3 occurs in the list four times, while the other values of 2, 4 and 5 each occur in the list two times.

Histogram of (2,3,3,4,5,4,3,5,2,3)

Histogram[{2, 3, 3, 4, 5, 4, 3, 5, 2, 3}]

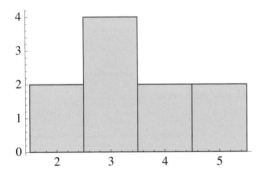

Mousing over the chart provides the frequency values, in addition to comparing the bars to the *y* axis.

A box-and-whisker chart is another type of chart used to gain insights into a list of numbers, and provides descriptive statistics values when the user mouses over the chart. The specific values for the max, median, min, 75% quantile and 25% quantile are displayed when mousing over the chart based on the list of numbers in the calculation.

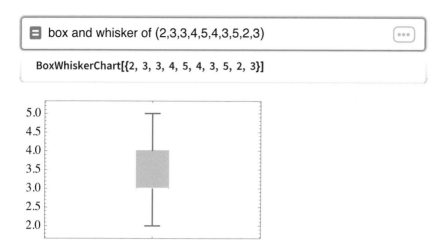

To graphically visualize a lengthy list of numbers, a pie chart can be used to compare each value against the total value of the list of numbers.

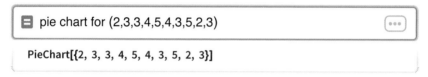

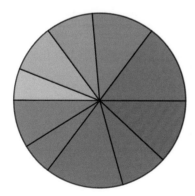

Clicking any one of the sections of the pie chart will break out that section from the rest of the pie chart for emphasis.

The software supports a variety of 3D graphics as well; adding the term "3D" at the beginning of the previous calculation creates a three dimensional pie chart.

▤ 3D pie chart for (2,3,3,4,5,4,3,5,2,3)  ⋯

PieChart3D[{2, 3, 3, 4, 5, 4, 3, 5, 2, 3}]

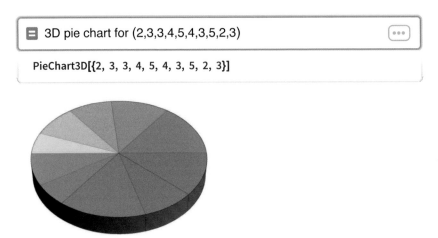

While a histogram provides insight into the frequency of values, a bar chart can be a useful way to visualize all the values in a large list of numbers, especially when the ordering of the values is significant.

▤ bar chart for (2,3,3,4,5,4,3,5,2,3)  ⋯

BarChart[{2, 3, 3, 4, 5, 4, 3, 5, 2, 3}]

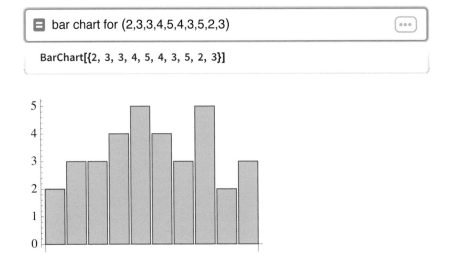

Adding the term "3D" at the beginning of a calculation that creates a bar chart will create a bar chart in three dimensions.

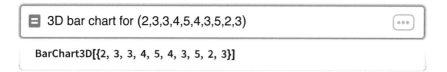

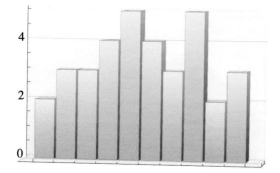

Any 3D chart can be rotated by clicking the chart, then dragging the mouse while continuing to hold down the mouse button.

A bubble chart can be used to visualize a more intricate list where each element in the list contains three values consisting of positions $(x, y)$, along with a size value that is the third element in each sublist. The following calculation shows that the size value of 25, which is graphed at position $(1, 1)$ is the largest size value in the list.

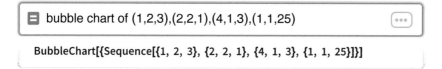

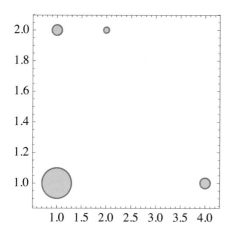

## Random Numbers and Probabilities

In addition to entering a list of numbers in a calculation, Wolfram|Alpha Notebook Edition can generate random numbers based on certain specifications. The following calculation generates a list of 10 random numbers, each with a value between 0 and 1.

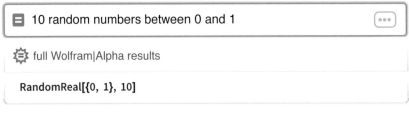

{0.930485, 0.180312, 0.563469, 0.133727, 0.0371245, 0.175538, 0.413255, 0.0375401, 0.551881, 0.443202}

The term "that" can be used to reference the last result, and the following calculation creates a graph of the list of random numbers. The graph confirms the values are evenly distributed and do not contain any discernable pattern.

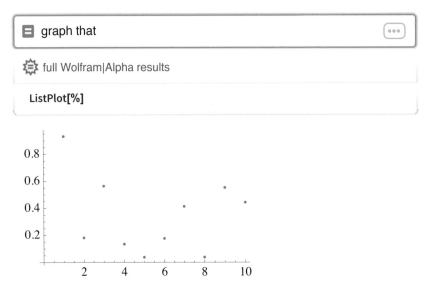

If the result of a calculation produces a lengthy list, the software automatically provides a subset of the data within a preview window, and will not print a large list of numbers to the screen. In the following example, the preview window displays only the first and last few values of the result, along with an abbreviation indicating the preview window is hiding 49,986 values of the list.

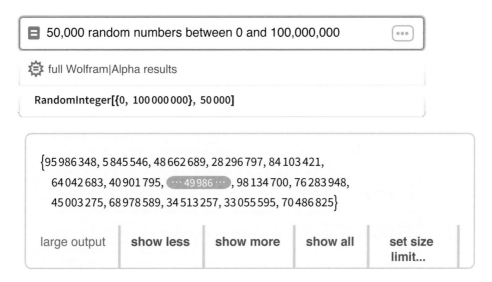

While the preview window does not display all the values, the lengthy list can be referenced with the term "that" to create a graph of all the values. This results in a dense graph of 50,000 points.

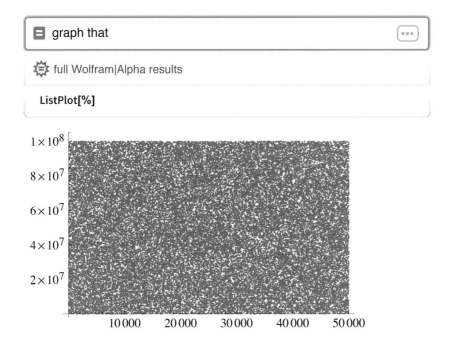

Because the calculations above generate random numbers, the results when the reader recreates these calculations will almost definitely be different. The results will be different if the calculations are reevaluated as well.

In addition to creating a list of random numbers, a calculation can select a random choice from a specific list of numbers.

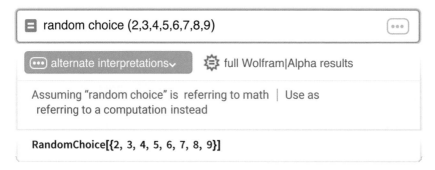

random choice (2,3,4,5,6,7,8,9)                                    ⋯

⦿ alternate interpretations⌄         ✦ full Wolfram|Alpha results

Assuming "random choice" is referring to math │ Use as referring to a computation instead

**RandomChoice[{2, 3, 4, 5, 6, 7, 8, 9}]**

4

A calculation can also use the same underlying technology to flip a coin. The result is formatted with an image of heads or tails along with a label. Rerunning this calculation will provide another independently random result.

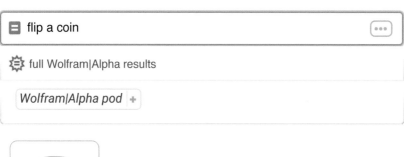

flip a coin                                                        ⋯

✦ full Wolfram|Alpha results

Wolfram|Alpha pod ✛

heads

Calculations in Wolfram|Alpha Notebook Edition return a single result. For certain calculations, however, the full Wolfram|Alpha results contain related calculations or graphics that are more useful than the single result in the software. Probability, and calculating the probability of the complement, is one example where Wolfram|Alpha Notebook Edition returns a general formula, while the full Wolfram|Alpha results return a collection of pods based on the specific calculation.

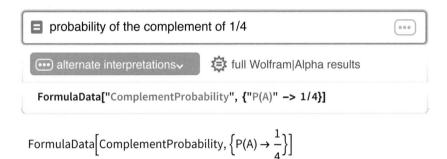

$$\text{FormulaData}\left[\text{ComplementProbability}, \left\{P(A) \to \frac{1}{4}\right\}\right]$$

### ⚛ probability of the complement of 1/4

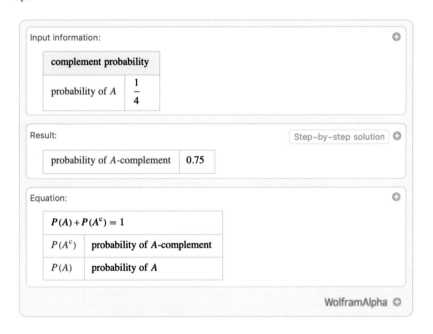

In addition to flipping a coin, calculations can involve dice of varying sizes. In the following calculation, the probability of rolling any of the four possible values on a tetrahedral die is shown graphically.

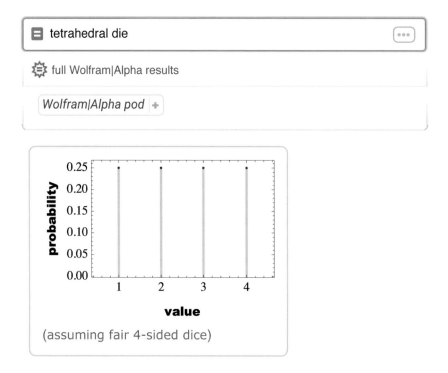

Changing "die" to "dice" updates the graph to reflect two tetrahedral die and the corresponding probabilities.

For certain problems, calculating probability is a multistep process. For example, calculating the probability that a roll of a tetrahedral die results in a prime number involves first calculating the quantity of prime numbers on the face of the die.

The term "tally" can be used to count specific cases in a list, so the phrase "tally that" returns an output of prime numbers and non-prime numbers on a four-sided die.

$$\begin{pmatrix} \text{False} & 2 \\ \text{True} & 2 \end{pmatrix}$$

 The results for the previous few calculations are not lengthy lists, so tallying the results might seem redundant. But this overall approach and phrasing can be very useful when a list is several times longer than the length of a computer screen.

To calculate the final probability, a simple substitution can be made with two possible outcomes for rolling a prime number out of four possible total outcomes. The calculation reduces the fraction to a probability of one-half.

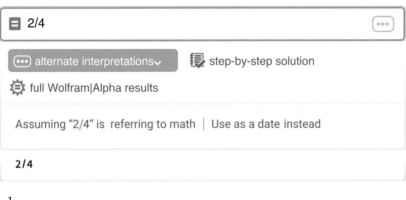

$$\frac{1}{2}$$

When calculating a probability requires an involved formula, storing an initial value with a symbol name can be a useful first step. In the following calculation, a fair coin is tossed seven times and the series of calculations will calculate the probability of five results of tails. The symbol *n* represents the quantity of coin tosses in the formula.

7

After *n* is defined, the binomial coefficient can be calculated using the following formula. The symbol *k* represents five results of tails when flipping a coin seven times.

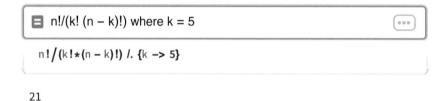

21

That result can be used to calculate the final probability and return the result as a decimal.

```
result/2^n
```

```
%/2^n
```

$$\frac{21}{128}$$

```
result as a decimal
```

```
N[%]
```

0.164063

The same series of calculations can be used to calculate the probability of five results of tails when tossing a coin 20 times instead of seven times.

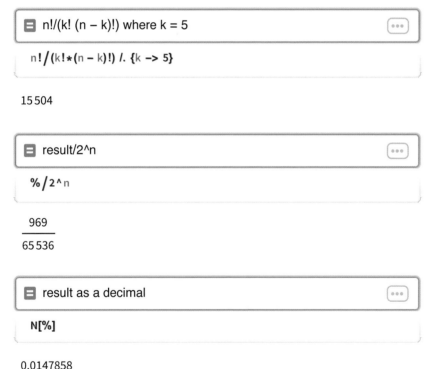

set n = 20

n = 20

20

> Remember that previous results will not change when redefining the symbol *n* with a new value unless those calculations are reevaluated after the new definition is stored. This makes it easy to copy and paste a series of calculations, change the initial value and create a new sequence of calculations using a new initial condition.

n!/(k! (n − k)!) where k = 5

n! / (k! * (n − k)!) /. {k -> 5}

15 504

result/2^n

% / 2 ^ n

$$\frac{969}{65\,536}$$

result as a decimal

N[%]

0.0147858

This result is a much lower probability compared to the first scenario. Wolfram|Alpha Notebook Edition is a useful environment to outline several scenarios to make comparisons and develop an intuition for overall concepts.

Calculations can also generate a list of permutations, which can be a useful component to calculating probabilities or a useful measure on its own. The following calculation shows all six permutations of two objects in a list of three total possible objects.

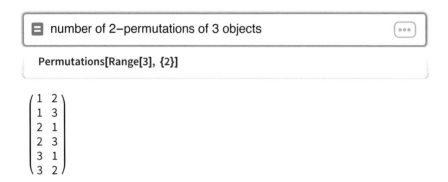

 Wolfram|Alpha Notebook Edition typically uses curly brackets to represent a list of results. However, if the result is a list of lists, the result will be formatted more like a table to make it easier to read.

Combinations are another useful measure in statistics, especially for areas like social media or analyzing website traffic. The following calculation shows there are 36 possible combinations of social media connections for nine friends, assuming each connection involves only two people.

```
▤  9!/(2!(9 − 2)!)                                    ⋯
   9! / (2! * (9 − 2)!)
```

36

# Correlation and Curve Fitting

Most of the examples so far in this chapter have calculated specific statistical tests. Wolfram|Alpha Notebook Edition can also be used to analyze trends in a dataset. The term "linear fit" can be used to calculate an equation of a line that best fits a dataset. This overall approach can be used to explore concepts like linear correlation or to predict values based on the overall pattern.

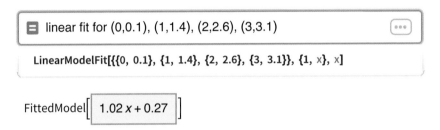

The **FittedModel** notation is specific to the Wolfram Language. When using the language directly, that provides a different set of advantages, but for the purposes of this chapter, subsequent calculations will simply use the $y = mx + b$ formatted equation for further graphics.

The term "graph" can be used to visualize the list of points and visually inspect the overall pattern.

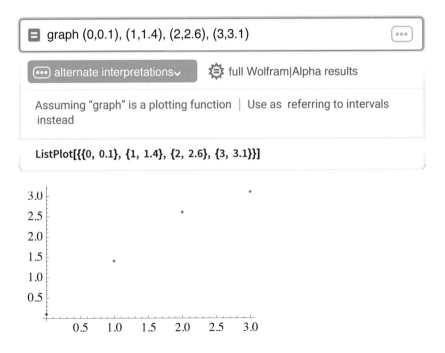

The following calculation shows a positive linear correlation through inspecting the graph of the line that best fits the dataset.

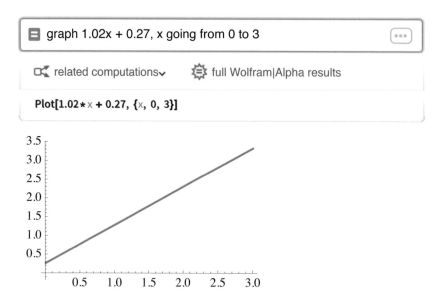

In addition to finding the equation of a line that best represents a dataset, calculations can find an equation for a curve that best represents a dataset if the relationship does not seem linear. The term "quadratic fit" can be used in a calculation to return a result with an equation involving an $x^2$ term.

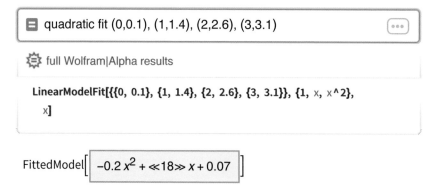

While similar individual calculations can be entered to create graphs for the original dataset as well as the curve that best represents the dataset, clicking the **full Wolfram|Alpha results** button displays a useful collection of pods, including a graph that shows both the raw data and the fitted curve.

**quadratic fit (0,0.1), (1,1.4), (2,2.6), (3,3.1)**

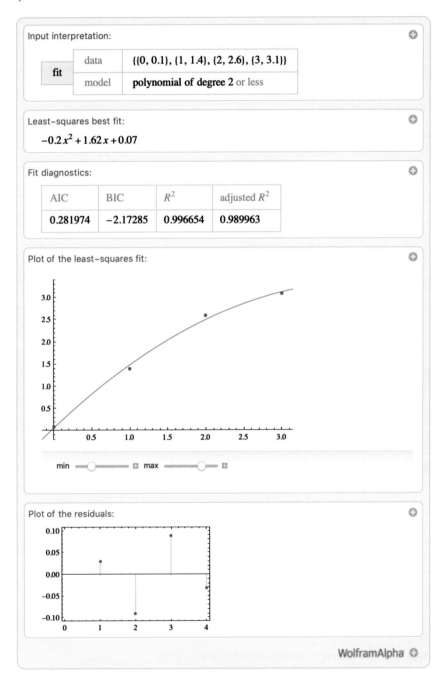

Input interpretation:

| fit | data | $\{\{0, 0.1\}, \{1, 1.4\}, \{2, 2.6\}, \{3, 3.1\}\}$ |
|-----|------|-----|
|     | model | polynomial of degree 2 or less |

Least−squares best fit:

$$-0.2\,x^2 + 1.62\,x + 0.07$$

Fit diagnostics:

| AIC | BIC | $R^2$ | adjusted $R^2$ |
|-----|-----|-------|----------------|
| 0.281974 | −2.17285 | 0.996654 | 0.989963 |

Plot of the least−squares fit:

min ⟶◯⟶ ⊞ max ⟶◯⟶ ⊞

Plot of the residuals:

WolframAlpha

In addition to visualizing the raw data with the fitted curve, a graph of the fit residuals shows how close the curve is to crossing the points in the original dataset.

Using the equation of the curve that best represents the data, new values can be calculated based on this relationship. The following calculation estimates the values of $y$ when $x$ is 4, 5 and 6 and returns a list of values in the result.

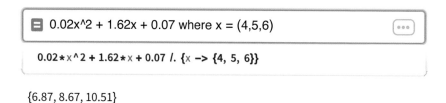

{6.87, 8.67, 10.51}

## Working with Distributions

Certain problems involving probabilities or representing real-world concepts through statistics involve distributions. The binomial distribution is the most commonly used distribution in precollege statistics, and the software has built-in knowledge of this distribution.

The following example calculates the probability that $x$ is greater than 4, if $x$ is distributed according to a binomial distribution with 10 trials and a probability of 0.5.

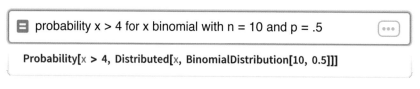

0.623047

A similar probability can be calculated when $x$ is less than 4, using the same distribution.

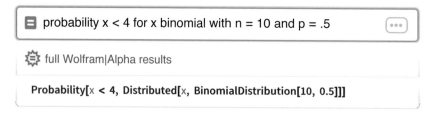

0.171875

The probability when $x$ equals 4 can also be calculated based on the same distribution.

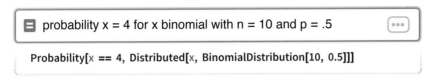

0.205078

Clicking the **full Wolfram|Alpha results** button in the previous calculation creates a new collection of pods with related calculations and graphics, mirroring the results on the Wolfram|Alpha website. For this particular calculation, the full Wolfram|Alpha results include a useful chart showing probabilities for other specific values of $x$.

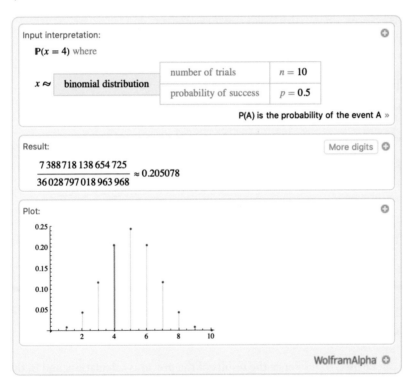

## Real-World Data

Wolfram|Alpha Notebook Edition contains a number of curated data sources that are built into the software. To aid in understanding statistics concepts, it is often useful to apply statistics tests to real-world data, and referencing this data within a notebook provides a consistent source for examples.

The following calculation returns a list of distances, all based on the city of Chicago, Illinois.

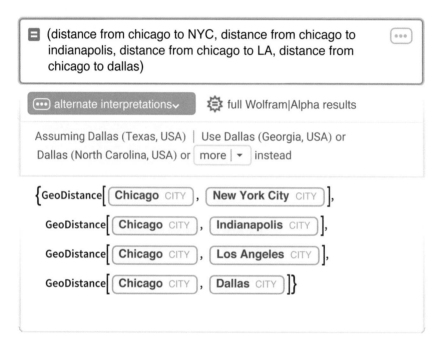

{696.442 mi, 147.749 mi, 1723.35 mi, 765.826 mi}

The unit of measurement is miles for the previous calculation, which can be clarified by hovering over any of the values.

The term "that" can be used to reference the results of the previous calculation, and in the following calculation, a mean is calculated based on the list of four distances.

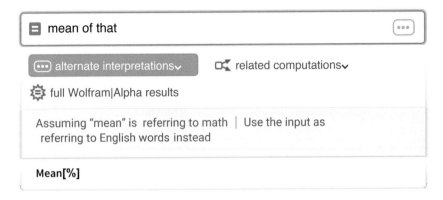

833.341 mi

The original calculation can be entered again, with a second calculation to create a graph of the list of distances.

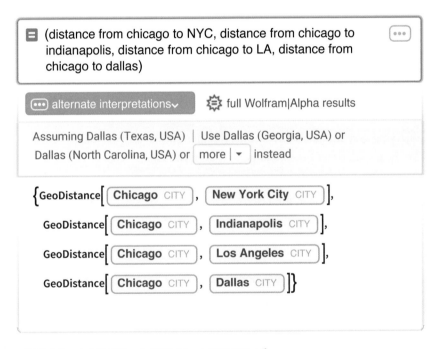

{696.442 mi, 147.749 mi, 1723.35 mi, 765.826 mi}

The original calculation is reentered just for clarity in this book; the reader could also go back and reevaluate the previous calculation to generate the list of distances instead of retyping or reentering the calculation. Remember the term "that" refers to the last evaluation, not the previous calculation on the page.

☰ graph that                                                             ···

ListPlot[%]

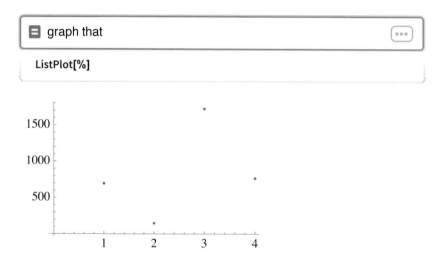

In addition to querying specific values one by one, broader queries are possible to return lists of values like the population of the 20 largest cities in the US.

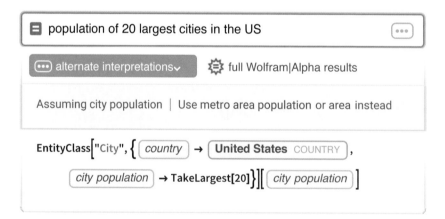

{8 622 698 people, 3 999 759 people, 2 716 450 people, 2 312 717 people,
     1 626 078 people, 1 580 863 people, 1 511 946 people, 1 419 516 people,
     1 341 075 people, 1 035 317 people, 950 715 people, 892 062 people,
     884 363 people, 879 170 people, 874 168 people, 863 002 people,
     859 035 people, 724 745 people, 704 621 people, 693 972 people}

The same approach can be used where the term "that" references the much lengthier list in the previous result, and creates a graph of the list of population values.

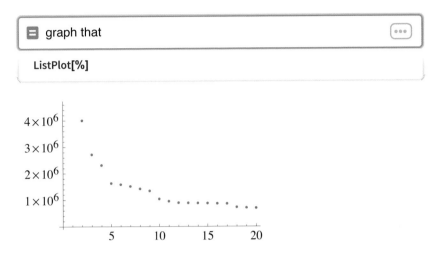

Repeating this calculation with the 100 largest US cities provides a different graph that is useful to compare to the first graph of the 20 largest cities in the US.

Instead of creating a graph of 20 population values, the original calculation can be entered again to then calculate the median value in the list of population values.

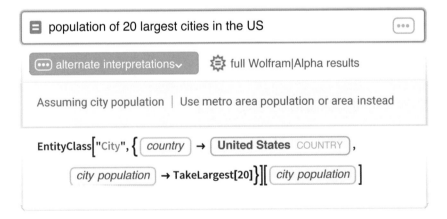

{8 622 698 people, 3 999 759 people, 2 716 450 people, 2 312 717 people, 1 626 078 people, 1 580 863 people, 1 511 946 people, 1 419 516 people, 1 341 075 people, 1 035 317 people, 950 715 people, 892 062 people, 884 363 people, 879 170 people, 874 168 people, 863 002 people, 859 035 people, 724 745 people, 704 621 people, 693 972 people}

993 016 people

 One general theme of this book is that notebooks provide a useful way to compare different calculations to gain insights. With this real-world data, comparing the median value to the graph above for all 20 population values can be an effective way to understand the overall concept of median values, and the advantages or disadvantages of using that particular statistic.

In addition to geographic data, Wolfram|Alpha Notebook Edition includes a variety of other types of data that can be useful to explore frequency of values. For example, a calculation can return naming frequency for specific names, showing the name Kelvin is used more frequently than Clifford.

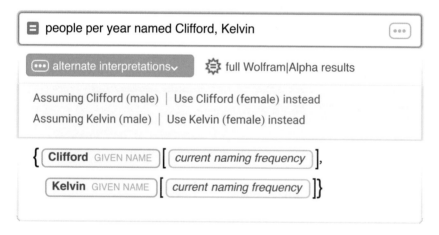

{143 people/yr, 280 people/yr}

The previous result shows the current naming frequency, but the **full Wolfram|Alpha results** button displays the naming frequencies over time. This demonstrates Clifford has been the far more popular name in terms of naming frequency over the past 140 years.

**people per year named Clifford, Kelvin**

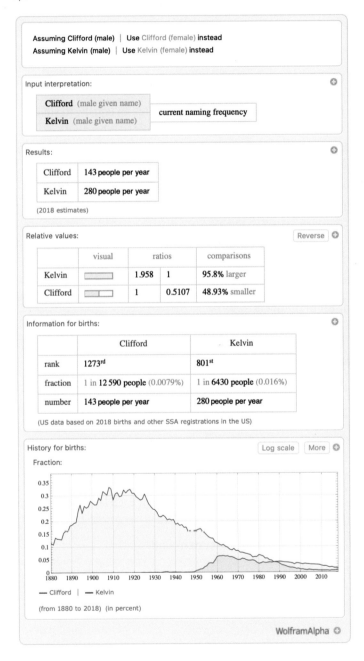

265

Some lessons in statistics involve analyzing whether a statistical measurement is misleading or not. A statistic can be misleading by providing a selectively small window in the duration of the data, or by providing selectively few factors. This would be an example; the statement "Kelvin is a more popular name than Clifford" is somewhat misleading since the name Clifford has historically been the far more popular name.

## Conclusion

In addition to calculations related to equations, notebooks provide an equally flexible environment for statistical calculations and visualizations. Use of real-world data or random number generation can also aid in the exploration of statistical concepts. As is the case for any chapter in this book, the ability to mix the various calculations with text explanations is also useful to outline a concept or prompt a student to outline their thoughts on a concept as a guided exercise.

## Exercises

1. Create a list of the first 10 prime numbers.

2. Find the average of that list of numbers.

3. Show the result as a decimal.

4. Copy and paste the first 10 prime numbers and graph them.

5. Find a linear fit of those numbers.

6. Graph that line of the linear fitted equation as $x$ goes from 0 to 10.

7. Find Charlie's free-throw percentage in basketball if the percentage is calculated as the number of made free throws divided by the total number of attempted free throws. In the season, Charlie has made 47 and attempted 73.

8. Find Sue's average lap time in the 1600 m race if her times for each lap (400 m) were 58 seconds, 1 minute, 1 minute 2 seconds and 57 seconds.

9. Convert the result from Exercise 8 from minutes to seconds.

10. Approximate the result in seconds.

# Index